The Turning Wheel

MAGICAL TALES & OTHER STORIES

Part One
The Wheel of the Year.
Tales, poems and meditations.

Part Two
Stories for a cold winter evening.

SUE THORNE

The Ever Turning Wheel

First published 2021 by Compass-Publishing UK

ISBN 978-1-913713-49-2

Copyright © Sue Thorne, 2021

A CIP catalogue record for this book is available from the British Library.

Printed and bound by The Design Hive

Cover design by © The Design Hive

FOREWORD

When I began my tales of the Village it was just going to be the first two stories. But then it grew and grew. Although the stories, poems and meditations in this little book follow the path of the Wheel of the Year they are not necessarily in the order that you would usually expect. I hope that you enjoy them.

The Village does exist. I have taken liberties with the locations, some are in South Devon and North Cornwall then we travel up the spine of England to the Peak District and then onwards to the Lake District and finally to Northumbria.

All of the characters in these stories are a figment of my imagination and are not based on any individual either living or dead.

For those of you who may be new to Paganism or may wish to find out more about our festivals this is the order we usually celebrate them in the Northern Hemisphere.

As you will read in the first poem, The Ever Turning Wheel, a Pagan year usually runs from Samhain to Samhain. Many Pagans mark the 1st November as the new year, myself included.

The dates of the festivals are as follows;

Samhain Sunset 31st October until Sunset 1st November.

Yule or Mid Winter Solstice, any time between Sunset 20th December and Sunset 22nd December, these are claimed to be the longest nights of the year.

Imbolc Sunset 31st January until Sunset 1st February.

Ostara or Spring Equinox. Any time around 20th March until Sunset 22nd March, day and night of almost equal length, from now on the days begin to get longer.

Beltaine or May Day Sunset 30th April until Sunset 1st May.

Summer Solstice, any time between Sunset 20th June until Sunset 22nd June, these are the shortest nights of the year.

Lughnasadh or Lammas Sunset 31st July until Sunset 1st August.

Mabon or Autumn Equinox any time around Sunset 20th September until Sunset 22nd September, once again day and night of roughly equal length, from now on the days begin to get shorter.

As you can see there is a festival each month, some are in the middle of the month others are spread across the cusp of two months. The festivals are roughly around six to seven weeks apart.

Part One

THE WHEEL
OF THE YEAR

TALES, POEMS AND MEDITATIONS

The Ever Turning Wheel

The Wheel turns from Samhain to Samhain. From Solstice to Solstice. The Oak and Holly kings do battle at Yule and at Summer's height. We sow. We reap. The Goddess appears as Maiden, Mother and Crone.

At Imbolc the Maiden Goddess first appears with beautiful Snowmaids at her feet. The Sun God is still small and weak but begins to find his way in the Wildwoods. The feast of Brighid is nigh. Lamb's milk drink is made, the froth in the cup overflowing. First lambs appear and gambol in the fields. The days begin to grow longer. The crocus raises its brave head it's pollen feeds the first bumble bees to emerge. Time to sow the seeds of our own ambition, what we would wish to achieve by Mabon.

Next is Ostara. The Goddess is grown. The God pays court, their union to complete, and the seed is sown. Spring is in full bloom. Boxing hares appear. Chocolate eggs bring delight to young and old as we hide them between the blooming golden daffodils. Tales of the Goddess, birds and hares are told.

At Beltaine we celebrate the wedding of the already pregnant Goddess and her Consort. The Green Man, Lord of the Wildwoods, Cernunnos, Herne, the Horned God call him what you will. With much dancing and merriment. Courting couples conjoin in the woods ready for Handfastings in June and July. The Hawthorn, the tree of the Goddess is in bloom.

Summer Solstice. The Goddess is in full bloom and the Sun God is at the height of his power. He strides across the sky from early morning until late in the evening. He brings awe to all during the long fun filled days of picnicking and games. Days of hay making and toiling upon the land. Bees are busy. They give us the gift of mead for our celebrations and the honey moon shines bright in the clear midnight sky. The Holly King challenges the mighty Oak King, surely the young pretender has no chance. Despite all odds the Holly raises his shiny thorny crown!

Lammas, Lughnasdah, Halfelmass brings forth first fruits of harvest. Our farmers labour long hard days to reap their crops of wheat, barley and rye. The God's blood is spilt upon the Earth and corn cockle, brilliant blue cornflowers and poppies grow in the field margins. We make our first loaves from the crop. Much ale and cider is consumed as the first harvest home is celebrated. The Goddess is both happy at the bounty of her harvest we are reaping and sad that her Lord is no more. She awaits his rebirth at the Winter Solstice.

Mabon sees our second harvest. A cornucopia of delights to sustain us through the long cold winter months ahead. We bottle, freeze and make jams and chutneys our harvest to preserve. The first apples are harvested for us to feast upon and store. Cider apples will come much later. Many ales are made and later will come the cheeses of apple juice for the cider. The Goddess is in the full bloom of her pregnancy though she turns her head to the left as Samhain approaches. It is the time for us to reap the harvests of the goals we set ourselves at Imbolc.

As Samhain dawns our Wheel has fully turned. The veil is thin between the worlds. Today is the day we honour our ancestors and remember those who have left us. The time of the Crone is upon us. The time to reflect upon our own mortality. The Lord of the Wildhunt seeks the souls of the departed to lead them across the Rainbow Bridge to the Summer Lands beyond.

Next is Yule our Midwinter Festival. A glimmer of hope in the darkness. The new Sun God is born to the Crone. The Oak King battles the reigning Holly King. The Oak is triumphant and his powers begin to grow over the next few months. Yule logs burn brightly in the long cold nights bringing cheer to our hearts and lives. Gifts are exchanged with love. Holly, ivy and mistletoe are picked with words of thanks to the Goddess to adorn our homes as we welcome the coming of the new infant God.

Summer Solstice

A VILLAGE TALE

*A*s the Summer Solstice approaches, the veil between the Worlds is thin. What Magick may be found upon a Summer Solstice Eve? The Fae Folk may dance in hidden woods and glades. The Lord of the Wildwood a Magickal web to weave. Read on my friends as this magickal tale unfolds.

"Here we go again." Thought Demi as she pushed her phone speakers even further into her ears. Demi had just arrived in South Devon for the annual Mid-Summer holiday with her parents. "Role on next year when I shall be sixteen and then I can stay at home and never ever have to endure this annual torture again." Sighed Demi.

As ever her parents Sarah and Mike were enthusing about the weeks ahead. The walks they would take and the wildlife they hoped to see and the ancient sites they hoped to find and explore. "Perhaps you would like to join us at Merryvale to explore with us, and afterwards we could have a lovely cream tea at Princetown, you would love it." Said her Mother. As ever Demi loathed the thought of spending time with her parents, after all what did they actually know. They had no ideas of how to dress, the meanings behind Rap music and the internet was just a tool to book a holiday and for emails. They hadn't a clue about the real world of video gaming, streaming and Youtube, that was where the real action and excitement was. Not stuck in some back water village in the middle of nowhere, where a mobile phone signal was non existent unless she walked miles into the village orchard and up a small hill. As for WIFI that was more miss than hit, and as for a cream tea, that was for old people. No mention of burger and chips which was proper food, something Demi rarely got to eat as her parents were into healthy eating in a big way. Oh next year she could have burgers and chips every day, for every meal if she wanted. Demi's mouth began to water at the sheer thought of it.

Demi longed for next Summer when she could stay at home alone and use the internet and TV as much as she wanted without her parents constant prying and fussing about trolls and old men grooming vulnerable young girls. As ever they had got it completely wrong, Demi was far too clever to be taken in by some disgusting old men.

After the unpacking of the car ritual, everything had to be packed and unpacked in a precise manner otherwise it put out the whole system. Demi had never quite figured out what the system actually was but that was old people for you. Demi sat on the bed in the room in the ancient thatched cottage that was to be home, or prison, as Demi thought of it for the next couple of weeks and sighed. All of her friends would be out and about enjoying themselves hanging out at McD's or just generally hanging and eyeing up the local talent. Not that there was ever much talent in the small seaside town where Demi and her parents lived. That is unless you counted the old men who insisted on wearing open toed sandals and socks paired with shorts that barely cleared their ankles. Not a good look and Demi was sure that the men in question would not be seen dead like that when they were at home so why did they have to inflict it upon her and her mates?

Demi checked her phone. As ever no signal just the legend, "Emergency Calls Only" that was a constant on her phone screen around here.

"Foods ready." Her Mother's voice drifted up the stairs, Demi made her way downstairs and plonked herself down on one of the dining chairs. "You could give your Mother a hand for once." Chided Mike. "After all we are all on holiday." He continued. Demi sighed and walked towards the kitchen. "Ah there you are." Said Sarah. "If you could just take the pepper in and this bowl of salad I will bring the quiche." Demi did as she was asked and then took her place once again at the table.

"Your Mother and I thought we would have a stroll around the village this evening and then pop into the pub for a drink, care to join us?" "Err no thanks Dad, I have to text Julie, I promised I would." Sarah and Mike exchanged glances, they just wished that Demi would join them occasionally for a walk or a day out and then she would see all of the things she missed in life. Wildlife, nature, trees and history. They hated how she shut herself in her room when they were at home let alone when they were away as a family. Obviously they knew it was teenage angst and that Demi would one day grow out of it and once more become the sweet natured girl she once had been before hormones had reared their ugly head. "OK, just as you wish." Replied Mike.

Endless day followed endless day. Demi's parents went out walking every day. The sun shone and the weather was perfect. Each day Demi spent the time in her room, not getting up until late every morning then making her own breakfast before wondering back to her room or up to the orchard to text and catch up with her mates.

Every day Demi's parents came home full of stories of their day, the things they had seen and the places they had visited. Demi listened totally bored by the whole thing. "It's the Summer Solstice on Wednesday." Said Sarah. "We shall be up and about early to watch the Sunrise then we plan to drive up onto the Moor to do some dowsing. It is the longest day of the year, please join us, you will really love it. Watching the Summer Solstice Sunrise is on everyone's to do list." Demi sighed. "Sorry Mum it's not on my to do list…….ever." "As you wish." If Demi had been looking closely she would have seen the hurt in her Mother's eyes. Demi was thinking about a guy she had seen around the village, he was rather good looking in a Country Bumpkin kind of way and she was wondering the best way she could "accidentally" bump into him.

On Monday when Demi's parents were safely out of the way Demi got up and showered and then wondered around the village in the hope that she would catch sight of her Country Bumpkin whose name she had learnt was Fin. Fin, it seemed, was a little older than Demi and was a bit of a Jack of All Trades. Decorating, gardening, grave digging and so on. Fin was also attractive in that he had transport. OK it was only a beat up old van but it had an engine and four wheels and it was actually capable of leaving the village.

Demi lingered outside of the General Store come Post Office come takeaway in the hope of seeing Fin so she could perhaps persuade him to take her out of the village. Demi's hopes were dashed when she overheard a couple of the villagers saying that Fin was out in one of the moorland villages doing a decorating job today. Downcast Demi made her way to the orchard to text her friends, desperate for some sort of contact with the Outside World as she thought of it.

All her friends were either busy or just not answering. Demi had no idea that her friends were beginning to ignore her texts and calls, they were becoming more than a little annoyed by her constant whinging about her holiday and her parents.

Demi wondered up through the orchard and saw a gate she had never noticed before. She paused and looked over the gate into some woodland that was strewn with large boulders that were covered in mosses and lichens. Not that Demi knew what it was she just thought it was green stuff and looked soft and interesting. Intrigued Demi opened the gate and walked towards the boulders. On closer inspection Demi noticed that the boulders were also covered in tiny cream coloured fossils. Even Demi knew a fossil when she saw one. Demi ran her hands over the hard granite rock and felt the raised areas where the fossils were and also stroked the soft dark green mosses, they felt cool and had a strange damp feeling and earthy kind of smell.

Demi continued along the path that lead through the trees. When the path forked she decided to take the right hand fork, if it wasn't the right way Demi reasoned she could turn around and follow the other fork to the left. In a very short while Demi came upon a boulder strewn clearing. Cascading over the boulders were small waterfalls and as Demi walked closer she could see a very large flat rock in the middle of the stream. By standing on a low wall Demi was able to jump onto the flat rock. As Demi looked up she could see that the tree cover was thinner here and where the sunlight pierced through the trees the boulder directly above her was pure white where no mosses or lichens grew. The granite glistened in the sunlight, it was almost dazzling as the light was reflected by the pale fossil shapes. Demi sat down upon the flat rock in amazement, she had never seen anything or anywhere quite so beautiful. The large flat rock she was sitting on was covered in soft dry mosses, Demi felt warm and comfortable and yes happy to be outdoors sitting on the flat rock in the middle of the wood.

Demi was not at all sure how long she sat in the wood but she realised she just had to return. Before she left Demi decided to take some photos of the Glade as she had named it. She clicked away happily with her phone thinking that when she was back in her room she could look at the pictures and once again capture the feeling of calm happiness she was feeling now.

Reluctantly Demi left the glade and walked back to the cottage, she noticed now for the first time the small apples beginning to form on the trees as she walked through the orchard, the stream that ran through the orchard and the wild flowers that covered the grass.

As Demi walked through the village towards the cottage to make herself some lunch she was smiling and said, "Good afternoon," to several of the villagers. Demi was in such a good mood that she didn't notice the villagers smiling and nudging one another and winking after she had walked past.

After a sandwich lunch Demi got out her phone to check the photos she had taken in the glade. Demi gave a small cry of dismay none of the photos she had taken were on her phone. Demi checked the battery strength and then realised that she had plenty of battery or her phone wouldn't turn on. "Very strange." Said Demi to herself.

Demi decided to walk back to the glade to take more photographs. Click, click, click. After each click Demi checked her phone, not one photograph was stored. Above the sounds of the waterfall and running water Demi was sure that she heard the sound of tinkling laughter, she turned around but no one was there. Click, click, click, once again not one photo and once again that now very distinctive laughter. "Phones don't work here." Said a voice. Demi turned around once more, again she saw no one around. "My imagination." Muttered Demi to herself.

After trying to take more pictures Demi decided to give up, there must be something wrong with her phone, she would get it sorted when she got home to civilisation she thought.

Demi sat quietly on an old fallen tree stump. Once again she was captivated by this place. Demi noticed how the trees had mosses growing all over their trunks and branches and out of the mosses there seemed to be ferns growing, lovely soft downy ferns. There were tall grasses and delicate pink flowers, hart's tongue fern and many other flowers and ferns Demi couldn't name. "Beautiful isn't it? I often come here to think or after a busy day." Demi started from her reverie. It was Fin. "Shove over." Said Fin as he sat beside Demi on the tree stump. Demi moved over to make space for Fin. "My phone won't work I wanted to take some pictures." Said Demi. "Oh no phones work here, not good in the whole village but they never work here." "Why not?" "Well because it's an enchanted Fairy Glade." Demi could barely contain herself. "Oh yes you laugh and mock. This whole Glade is home to the Fae Folk. Can't you feel it in the air, the enchantment, the atmosphere, the Spirit of the place?" Asked Fin.

Reluctantly Demi nodded her head, she had to agree that the place was indeed magical and had a special feeling.

"It's Solstice Eve tomorrow, you meet me here at 9 o'clock in the evening and we can watch the sunset together." Demi wasn't at all sure about this, remembering her mockery of her parents when they had suggested she watch the Solstice Sunrise but she did want to be with Fin. "OK, 9 o'clock tomorrow evening then." Fin got up and stretched. "See you." Before Demi could reply he was gone.

The following morning Demi was again up early, her parents were amazed. "Are you planning to come out with us for the day?" Asked Sarah. "Well no." Said Demi. "I was planning to go for a long walk by myself around here, to explore the area." Demi's Mother and Father were too shocked to reply and merely nodded. "Well we are off now, enjoy your day." Said Mike a short while later as they were leaving. "Oh I will." Said Demi smiling.

"Well that's a turn up for the books." Said Mike when they had shut the front door of the cottage. Sarah smiled. "I just wonder if she has found the Glade and it has worked it's magic?" "Ah yes you could be right." Agreed Mike. "I have noticed a difference in her over the past couple of days." "We shall see." Said Sarah. "It's Solstice Eve today."

Demi was humming to herself as she showered and tidied her room. For the first time she had noticed that her room was a complete shambles and floordrobe couldn't begin to describe the mess. When Demi went downstairs she tidied the living room and decided to make herself a sandwich and a drink to take out with her on her walk. Then without thinking she cleared up the kitchen too.

Demi put her lunch into a spare rucksack and set off.

Demi headed towards the orchard. The thought of phoning

or texting her friends never entered her head, she was eager to head off to the glade.

When she reached the glade Demi stopped again to take in the beauty and the sheer peace that fell over her whenever she came there.

After some while Demi headed up out of the glade, clambering over the huge boulders that were strewn across the hillside. Demi hadn't a clue where she was going it was as though some hidden force was driving her on. As she walked Demi noticed the trees, suddenly she knew their names. Oak. Ash. Beech. Silver Birch. Demi thought I must have seen the names in a book at some point and now it's just registering what they are. Demi was so absorbed in her walk and the trees that she didn't notice the faces and eyes in the trees as she walked past. The Tree Sprites watched as she passed by. Tree branches moved subtly as if bending in the breeze, but gently guiding Demi along their chosen route. On and on Demi walked until she came to a clearing. She noticed that all of the ferns which were waist high everywhere else had been cut down and there were large stones everywhere. Demi started in surprise to see her parents. "Hello!" She called. "Hello to you." Said Sarah and Mike. "What brings you here?" "Well I was just walking and I seemed to have been drawn to this place." "This is an old Iron Age settlement." Said Mike. "We are dowsing the area, want a try?" Demi was amazed. "Well yes I'll have a go." Mike showed Demi how to hold the rods and told her the areas to walk. Demi was more than a little surprised to find that the rods moved so easily in her hands and crossed over without any hesitation when she passed over certain areas. "Awesome." Demi was almost unable to believe that this could be happening. To test it wasn't a fluke or her imagination Demi rewalked the route and again the rods crossed in the same places.

Demi realised that by now she had walked some way and she was very hungry. Mike looked at his watch. "I'm famished.

Lunch time." Sarah and Mike sat down on some of the rocks, to their surprise and absolute delight Demi joined them. They all tucked into a packed lunch. Mike explained that the area had once been an Iron Age village settlement, "Can you see the round circles where the houses once stood?" Demi stood up and from there she could make out the hut circles. "Oh yes I can, isn't it amazing. How long have they been here?" "About four thousand years." Answered Mike. Demi struggled to take in this information. "Four thousand years?" "Yes that's right."

Much to her amazement Demi spent the afternoon with Mike and Sarah. The time just flew by and before she knew it, it was time to head for home. "Care to join us at the pub for supper this evening." Asked Sarah. "Yes I would love to but I have a date of sorts." Demi felt instantly guilty about meeting Fin to watch the Solstice Eve Sunset when she had turned her parents down flat when they suggested she join them for Solstice Sunrise.

"A date?" Queried Mike. "Well yes there's a guy named Fin in the village and he asked me to watch the sunset this evening at 9 o'clock." "Oh we plan to watch it too." Said Sarah "So we shall have eaten way before that." "If you don't mind." Mumbled Demi, "Of course not." Said Mike.

Demi was surprised at how much she enjoyed the meal and her parent's company and the stories of walks, nature and the ancient sites that they had spent dowsing over the past few days. "I didn't realise how interesting it all is." Demi began to feel very ashamed of herself as she realised how badly she had treated Sarah and Mike.

"It's nearly 9 o'clock. Time you met Fin." "Oh I didn't realise the time." Demi hugged her parents and dashed off towards the glade.

"The Glade magic is working." Said Sarah. Mike nodded. "Yes such a change in so short a time the magic must be extra strong this year." "Well not only is it Solstice Eve, it is a Full Moon tonight." Replied Sarah. "Oh yes I can't believe

I forgot."

Demi ran up through the orchard towards the Glade. She was running so fast she almost missed seeing Fin. He was sitting cross legged on one of the large boulders that dotted the orchard. "Eh now, no need to rush. Sunset's not for at least another half an hour, come climb up over to the top of the hill with me, we won't see anything in the orchard or the glade it's too low down." Demi and Fin walked together in companionable silence up towards the top of the hill. Once at the top they leaned on a five bar gate to look across at the whole valley where the village lay and out towards Dartmoor in the distance. "Not long till sunset now." Said Fin. Whilst they were waiting for the sunset Demi couldn't resist stealing a quick look at Fin. He really was very good looking, his face was very tanned, he had a mop of curling red hair and the most amazing green eyes Demi had ever seen.

Fin knew that Demi was looking at him, he had that effect on all the girls and women who had ever met him.

Suddenly Fin pointed towards the distant horizon. "There the Sun is setting it's the beginning of the shortest night of the year." Demi was amazed, she couldn't believe the beauty and the range of colours in the sky. Reds, yellows, oranges and golds all seemed to intermingle but also seemed to stand out alone. All on a pale blue background. "Wow!" Was the only word Demi could manage. "Now turn around and look behind you." Said Fin. Demi turned around, she let out yet another gasp of amazement for the Full Midsummer Moon was just beginning to ride in the sky. "She will shine long and bright this magical night." Said Fin. Demi stood in wonderment gazing at the Moon in all her glory.

"Now come with me to the Glade." Demi looked at Fin. He looked somehow different in this light, his hair was shining in the moonlight and she was sure she could see some Ivy in his hair that she hadn't noticed before. "Oh yes." Breathed Demi. Quickly Demi and Fin walked down the hill to the Glade.

"Sit there." Commanded Fin as he placed her gently upon the flat stone in the middle of the stream. Was it her imagination yet again or could she hear voices, and also she thought some music. "Must be kids playing music on the road above us." Thought Demi. But no, the music and the voices were coming closer and closer and suddenly small lights lit up the Glade and the voices and music became clearer and clearer. Suddenly Demi's feet began to tap she wanted so much to dance. Demi looked across to where she had last seen Fin. Was it Fin? Fin now looked so different, gone were the old jeans he had been wearing. Instead Fin was covered in a cloak of Ivy, Oak and Holly leaves, his red hair shone in the moon and lamplight. His green eyes flashed, he looked across to Demi. "Yes come and dance in the greenwood on this shortest night of the year. Come join us the Fey folk for I am the Lord of the Greenwood, and this is my domain, all who come here feel my magic and power."

Demi got to her feet. Her feet just wouldn't stop tapping and moving as if they were spellbound. Demi danced and danced. She danced with Fin, she danced alone, she danced with the Fey Folk. The night truly was magical. Demi laughed and laughed as she swirled and twirled. All too soon it seemed to Demi the magical night ended, the music stopped and the lights faded. Demi looked up and was surprised to see streaks of daylight beginning to appear. "Come and watch the Solstice Sunrise." Fin said. Demi followed Fin back towards the top of the hill her sore feet forgotten. Several people had already arrived including Sarah and Mike. "Oh great you made it." Said Sarah. "I hope your feet aren't too sore after all the dancing." Her Mother laughed. Before Demi could reply the Sun began to emerge in the far distance. Just a tiny yellow tip at first but then quickly becoming a bright yellow and gold disc and rising ever faster in the early morning sky. "Summer Solstice Blessings!" They all cried in unison, even Demi, totally surprising herself. Demi looked across to where

Fin had been standing. To her dismay Fin had disappeared. "Where is Fin?" Demi asked the nearest person to her. "Oh he be gone now for a while my dear. We shall see him again in a short time. Don't you be going and falling for him though, many a maiden's heart he has broken over the ages." Demi couldn't quite believe what she was hearing. Sarah had been watching her daughter, she saw Demi's face fall. Quickly she went to her daughter's side and put her arm around Demi's shoulder. "Don't you fret and get upset. Fin is all around us everywhere in this Village. The Village is Fin, if there was no Fin there would be no Village. He is the Spirit of this place, the Lord of the Greenwood and the Lord of the Wild hunt. He will be back." Demi looked at her mother gazing deeply into Sarah's eyes. Suddenly Demi understood why her parents, and especially her mother, was drawn to this place year after year for the Summer Solstice. Sarah nodded. "Yes. I too once danced on Summer Solstice Eve with the Lord of the Greenwood." Demi nodded. "I can't wait to come back next year."

SUMMER SOLSTICE SUNRISE

I steal from my bed in dawn's early light. Summer Solstice Sun to greet. All is silent in eerie half light. The dawn chorus is yet to begin. Quietly I dress so not to wake a small dog sleeping near.

As I creep to the door I hear a small sound. I turn and there is my true and faithful friend. "OK." I say. I open the door and we both walk out into the ever growing daylight.

As we walk through long grass soaking wet with dew, we hear the beginnings of the bird's pre-sunrise song. Blackbird has indeed spoken as this new dawn has broken.

We climb steadily to the top of a small hill, our eyes ever gazing north east.
As we wait patiently for the sun to lighten the far horizon we stand shivering in the early morning light.

Suddenly the sun is there spreading fingers of gold, red and orange light as it appears on this new day. Our patience rewarded I stand hands held high to greet the Sunrise upon this special morn.

SUMMER SOLSTICE MEDITATION

Sit quietly where you won't be disturbed. Take a drink to ground yourself when you return. Light a candle or some incense if appropriate. Adjust your clothes and get comfortable…….

Close your eyes and begin to relax………….

When you are ready to begin concentrate on your breathing. Take in a deep breath. Breathe in through your nose. Take the breath deep into your body. Breathe out through your mouth. Breathe in through your nose and out through your mouth, once more in through the nose and out through the mouth. Now still concentrating on your breathing begin to breath naturally………..

You are standing on a lawn above a wild flower meadow….. It is just before sunrise at the Midsummer Solstice….. All around is silence….. You feel calm and peaceful….. You see the soft pink streaks of light just beginning to show on the horizon…….. Suddenly, as if by magic, the birds begin to sing. Blackbird…Robin…Thrush…Sparrow…Wren. Voices raised to greet the coming sunrise……

Remove your shoes and stand barefoot upon the cool mossy grass…………..

Look to the horizon and the sun is just beginning to show……………. It's golden orange glow bathing the fields in soft light. Greet the sunrise……………..

If you look to your left you will see Glastonbury Tor. Many people are at the top of the Tor gazing in wonder at the new Solstice sunrise…………..

Look down and see the blades of grass between your toes……………..

All around you is now filled with the golden light of the sun, it warms the Earth and surrounding landscape in it's full Midsummer glory.

The wild flowers in the meadow are in full bloom. Ox eye daisy, pink campion, cornflowers, bright red poppies all nod in the gentle breeze as it stirs the long grasses……………..

As you look at the flowers and grasses you see Bees, hover flies and numerous butterflies of many colours all busy going from bloom to bloom to collect pollen and nectar……………..

The Sun is now much higher in the sky and the morning is becoming increasingly warm. Walk slowly down the path past the wild flower meadow to the shallow pool on the lawns below……………….. Gingerly dip your toes in the water. It is cool and refreshing. You decide to stand in the water…………. As you look down you see ripples of water around your feet and toes……….. The water is crystal clear……….. It makes you feel invigorated and cleansed………….. Step out of the pool onto the short grass of the lawn. Droplets of water on your feet glisten, light reflecting like small diamonds upon your feet and toes……………..

When your feet are dry replace your footwear and walk across the lawn to the majestic yews. Here you pause awhile with your hands on the bark of the tree. The bark is rough and textured. Feel the course bark with your fingers. Feel the life energy of the tree. Breathe deeply enjoying the scents of the wood and leaves…………….

Now walk to the statue of the Goddess and stand. You see the many offerings that have been placed before or in the statue. Place your own offering……Stand now awhile to see if the Goddess has a message for you………….

Now turn to face the pool once more. You feel calm and at peace as you begin to leave this beautiful space................

When you are ready slowly begin count down from five. Move your shoulders and head from side to side as you come back to the room. If you lit a candle when you blow it out send love and healing to those in need and take a moment to reflect upon the season. Take some small sips of water to ground yourself.

For those of you familiar with Glastonbury. This meditation is based in the beautiful Chalice Well gardens.

Lughnasadh

A VILLAGE TALE

*A*s *The Lord of the Greenwood my year it runs thus;*
Samhain is my Harvest of Souls. Those who have passed
I lead across the Rainbow Bridge from our World into theirs,

At Yule I return to be reborn, a witness as the great Holly and Oak Kings do battle,

At Imbolc the Maiden returns with the first bloom of the Snowdrops, a helpless child am I,

At Ostara the Maiden is honoured and I am now full grown, our union for to seal,

At Beltaine I wed my Lady of the Greenwood so fair,

At Litha my powers are at their height but thereafter I begin to wane,

At Lughnasadh I am slain to spill my blood upon the corn, to be raised up again by my fair Lady Demeter,

At Mabon, second harvest, much merriment and feasting will follow as the Lady's bounty is for all to partake, now she is turning her head to the left, her sorrow for to hide,

Then again my third harvest at Samhain as The Wheel ever turns.

Demi carefully packed her holdall. Several years had now passed since the momentous events at the Summer Solstice when Demi had first met the enigmatic Fin on the annual family holiday to a small village in South Devon. Since then Demi had done a great deal of growing up especially since her mother Sarah had become very ill. Thankfully Sarah had now been given the all clear and this holiday was by way of a celebration.

Usually Demi and her parent's, Sarah and Mike, spent several weeks at their favourite holiday cottage around the Summer Solstice, but over the past couple of years holidays had been short breaks to Devon around Sarah's treatment program. Instead of a holiday in June the family were spending a couple of weeks at the cottage at the end of July into August.

Demi began once again to think of Fin. Despite many warnings over the years not to fall for Fin Demi had indeed fallen in a big way. She hoped against hope that Fin felt the same way but Fin never gave anything away.

Over the years Demi had tried University but gave up after six months deciding that a degree just wasn't for her. Instead she had attended catering college and after graduating began working as a pastry chef in a large local restaurant. When Sarah had become ill Demi had started to run her own successful celebration cakes and outside catering business from home. She juggled the business around Sarah's treatment plans as Mike's career took him away from home a great deal.

During the journey to Devon Sarah and Mike glanced at each other several times, they had noticed how preoccupied Demi had become since they set off from home. Both of them knew how Demi felt about Fin and worried about her future.

After unpacking Demi went for a short walk through the village towards the orchard and then into the Glade. The waterfalls as ever flowed over the sandy pebbles and the many boulders in the glade. Demi stepped across to the flat rock where she had been standing the first time she had met Fin, when she had been trying unsuccessfully to take some photos all those years ago.

"You are back at last then?" Demi whirled around, she knew that unmistakable voice. "Fin!" Demi cried. It was all she could do to stop herself rushing towards him to give him a hug. Over the years Fin had made it quite plain that theirs was to be a platonic friendship only. "Oh its so good to see you again. I have so missed seeing you and this special enchanted place."

"How is your Mum?" "Oh much, much better, she has just been given the all clear so we have come away to celebrate the fantastic news." Replied Demi.

"Good news indeed." Agreed Fin.

Demi had so many questions for Fin but voiced none of them. Instead she asked. "How have you been, what news of the Village?"

"Oh I have been OK and the village is as it ever was. The Wheel has turned with no endings or beginnings." Said Fin ambiguously. Demi was not at all sure she understood exactly what Fin meant. Of course Demi knew that the Village was a very special, almost magical place, and that Fin never seemed to age. If anything Demi now felt she was older than Fin, she knew that couldn't be true, when she had first met Fin over six years ago Demi was still at school and Fin was old enough to drive.

"Well I'll be off, see you around." With that Fin seemed to just disappear into the woodland surrounding them.

Demi remained where she was for a while longer enjoying the peace and quiet of her special space, then she too left and wondered back to the cottage where Sarah and Mike were waiting for her to go to the pub for supper.

"Nice stroll?" Asked Mike. "Mmm yes thanks. I bumped into Fin." Sarah and Mike exchanged a glance then Mike said. "Come on pub's open for food and I'm ravenous."

Later that evening as Sarah and Mike prepared for bed Sarah asked Mike if they should tell Demi about why the village kept calling them back year after year and the truth about Fin. "I feel that the time could be right." Said Mike

As ever when Demi was on holiday in the village the days seemed to merge into one another. Long walks and lazy picnics followed by a glass of chilled wine with supper.

Since that first day when they had arrived Demi hadn't seen Fin. On her walks Demi often thought of Fin and as she was now older she thought of how life would be if they could only get together.

That evening over supper Demi commented to Sarah and Mike about how very special the village was and she thought she could understand why her parents loved the area so much.

Sarah looked at Mike who nodded. Sarah drew a deep breath and said. "Yes the village is a very special place. We first came here over twenty two years ago on our honeymoon. We fell in love with the place and it has always held a very special space in our hearts." Demi thought she knew the reason for this as she had known for years that she had been conceived on Sarah and Mike's honeymoon.

"As you know." Continued Sarah. "You were conceived here, but what you don't know it was a Summer Solstice full moon and there was a very special magic that night as we lay together in the glade." "You mean?" Began Demi, Sarah smiled, "Yes you were conceived that night in the glade. We feel that is why you find the place so special and magical, and of course your birthday is at the feast of Ostara."

Demi knew that her birthday was at a very special time of the year. When she was a child growing up, all that Demi knew was her birthday was either at Easter or near to it. To Demi all that really meant was school holidays and chocolate eggs, the highlight of any child's year but now things were starting to become clearer.

"So that is why you come here year after year and why this place is so special to you both." Demi suddenly felt very mean thinking back to all of the times when she had hated coming to the village for her holidays, how a few years ago she had really upset her parents by being so difficult. If only she had known perhaps she would have been much kinder.

"What you don't know," Continued Sarah. "Is that I always used to come here for holidays with my parents too and only stopped coming here when I met your Dad, it was only on a whim to see this place again I suggested we had our first married holiday together here. Demi suddenly remembered back to the holiday a few years ago when her mother had said she had danced at Midsummer Eve in the Glade with the Lord of the Greenwood.

Sarah and Mike could see that Demi was deep in thought and were not sure if they should continue when Demi asked Sarah. "So you said you had danced in the Glade when you were younger, who did you dance with, was it the locals?" Though as Demi asked the question she thought she already knew the answer. "I danced, as you did, a few years ago with the Lord of the Greenwood and the sprites and spirits of the woodlands. I danced with Fin as have countless other young girls over the years."

"Fin?" Demi couldn't quite believe what her mother was saying. "But Fin is a young man, just a few years older than me…...How could you be dancing with him, he must be ancient by now if that is true." "Surely you remember that Fin is the Lord of the Greenwood. Yes he is both ancient and young, can you not remember the order the Wheel turns as we celebrate at home?"

Demi knew that her parents celebrated the holidays of the turning year. Although she joined in with them when she was able, she hadn't really been following exactly the seasons and what happened as each holiday was marked.

"Tomorrow is Lughnasadh." Said Sarah. "I think that you need to come up to the wheat fields with us to see exactly what goes on during the ceremony. I will warn you though that you will be in for a big shock." Demi stared at Sarah and Mike. "What do you mean, a big shock, isn't it just drinking mead and cider and eating a ploughman's lunch?" Again Demi wished she had taken more notice of the ceremonies over the years. "All will be explained tomorrow." Replied Mike enigmatically and with that neither of her parents would be drawn further.

The following day dawned sunny and fine and all of the village were up early to make their way up to the wheat fields for the final cut of the harvest for that year. The smell of fresh baked bread and cakes drifted on the air making Demi feel very hungry indeed. As Demi followed on behind she reflected it was nice for once that someone else had done the baking. When they arrived at the fields several trestle tables had been set up and all the food and drink was being set out ready for the festivities. Demi couldn't understand why Sarah and Mike had said she would have a shock, it all looked like a very innocent village gathering. Just then the combine stopped leaving just the last few yards of wheat standing. Everyone became silent and full of expectation. The villagers as one formed a large circle holding hands and then began to dance and chant. At first Demi couldn't understand what everyone was singing but then the words became clearer.

"The Corn King is here, his sacrifice to bear,
With scythes and knives we shall cut him down,
His blood to spill upon the Earth, her fertility to restore,
Up again he shall be raised to live again once more"

Demi, Sarah and Mike joined in the circle dancing and chanting. Demi felt as though she was almost being hypnotised by the rhythm. Suddenly the dancing and chanting stopped. Three burly men approached the circle dragging a fourth man, the three men held scythes above their heads, they each had a knife in their belt. The fourth man struggled and kept his head lowered. As they reached the circle a gap was created and all four men went into the centre of the circle amongst the remaining ears of wheat. As Demi watched Sarah also walked to the centre of the circle. "Who orders the sacrifice of the Corn King?" The leader of the men asked. "I Hecate, Priestess order it!" Commanded Sarah. Demi stared at her mother, she was transformed from her usual calm kind self to someone totally unrecognisable. She had almost grown in stature and was dressed in black robes. The three men threw the fourth man to the ground and catching him by his shoulder length red hair pulled his head back to bare his neck for all to see. Demi sobbed the breath catching in her throat. "No!" She tried to shout but no words came. Before Demi could do anything more the three men cut Fin's throat and his blood poured forth onto the last of the wheat soaking the land all around. "It is done! I Hecate Priestess of the night have ordered the slaying of the Corn King so that the Land will be fertile once more. Who amongst you will raise him up and feed him with bread and wine?"

Demi felt Mike give her a gentle push. "Go Demeter, this is what you are here for. This is your destiny." Demi stumbled forward, almost blinded by her tears of sorrow and rage. "Come take his hands in yours and raise him up." Said Sarah. Demi walked towards Fin and bending over him took his hands in hers. To her surprise Fin tightly gripped Demi's hands as she raised him to his feet his neck and chest still covered in blood. Someone placed some bread in Demi's hand. "Come eat this bread, what has come from the Land goes back to the Land to restore fertility to the Land." Demi then offered a chalice filled with red wine to Fin. "What has come from the Land goes back to the Land to restore fertility to the Land. I Demeter command you. Drink!" Demi had no idea where the words came from. As she looked at Fin she could see that already his fatal wounds were beginning to heal. Fin turned to her and smiled his wonderful smile. After eating the bread and drinking the wine Fin was bourne away by a group of Elder women from the village.

"Come child and have some bread and mead." Demi turned to see her mother totally restored to her normal self. "No questions now. Later."

The rest of the day passed in a blur. Demi joined in the

feasting and the games and singing and dancing but all of the time she couldn't rid herself of the image of Fin being slaughtered and then raising him up again.

Later that evening, when everyone had gone home, Demi decided that she needed some quiet time to think upon all that had happened that day. She found herself drawn to her usual place of comfort and solitude. As she walked to the glade her mind was buzzing with questions. Suddenly Demi realised that she was not alone, she turned and realised that Fin was walking up behind her. "I figured I find you here." "Fin!" Demi rushed towards Fin and threw her arms around him, the tears held in check all day spilling over. "What happened earlier? Where is all of the blood? Why aren't you dead?" Demi stopped, that last question was not tactful she realised.

"Come and sit with me maid and I will explain." Answered Fin. Hand in hand they made their way to the Glade.

When they were sitting on Demi's favourite fallen tree trunk Fin turned to her. "You must know that I am the Lord of the Greenwood, the Corn King, what others may call the Green Man, the Horned God? You have danced with me and the Fey folk on Midsummers Eve and now today you have witnessed me being slain by the Three Reapers at the command of Hecate, who this year was your own Mother as she also has recently cheated death's cold grip." Demi at last realised that yes indeed she had known these things, suddenly she realised that Fin was speaking again;

"As The Lord of the Greenwood my year it runs thus;

Samhain is my Harvest of Souls. Those who have passed, I lead across the Rainbow Bridge from our World into theirs,

At Yule I return to be reborn, a witness as the great Holly and Oak Kings do battle,

At Imbolc the Maiden returns with the first bloom of the Snowdrops, a helpless child am I,

At Ostara the Maiden is honoured and I am now full grown our union for to seal,

At Beltaine I wed my Lady of the Greenwood so fair,

At Litha my powers are at their height but thereafter I begin to wane,

At Lughnasadh I am slain to spill my blood upon the corn, to be raised up again by my fair Lady Demeter,

At Mabon, second harvest, much merriment and feasting will follow as the Lady's bounty is for all to partake, now she turns her head to the left her sorrow for to hide,

Then again my third harvest at Samhain as The Wheel ever turns."

As Demi listened she realised that Fin indeed was all of these things. She couldn't understand it all but she felt as in everything in the village it was magic. "But how was I able to raise you up and what appears to have healed you?" "Because Demeter you are the Chosen One, the One it was ordained at your conception, would be here help me on my journey through the Wheel. You would be the One to bear, when the time comes, the new Lord of the Greenwood for not even I am destined to live forever. Demi was struggling to take in all of this information. It was rare that her full name was used. "But how old are you? Does that mean we are a couple now? Are we to be married?" "Questions, questions, questions." Laughed Fin

Again Demi felt her mind would explode trying to take in everything she had witnessed and now heard on this amazing day. Demi realised that Fin was speaking again;

"On my journey through the eternal Wheel of Life shall you be by my side. Maiden, Mother and Crone. As I am reborn each Lughnasadh so shall your beauty be restored at Imbolc, in March at Ostara we shall become one, at Beltaine we shall celebrate as the Lord and Lady of the Greenwood. At Litha you shall be

blooming whilst I hold full power over the length of days, at Lughnasadh you shall raise me, at Mabon your harvest will be fullsome, the Cornucopia of bounty forthcoming, at Samhain the Wild Hunt I shall lead, by now a Crone you shall be, at Yule we shall witness the rebirth of the Sun God for that is the way of the Wheel"

"Are you willing to fulfil your destiny Demeter. To be by my side throughout the long years as we follow the Wheel's turning together. To experience the changes of your body to be Maiden, Mother and Crone?"

"How will this be possible for surely we shall both become old and die one day?" "Yes we shall die one day and you shall give birth to a new Lord of the Greenwood in the future. Until then if you stay by my side, you, like me will have eternal life. For this to happen we must stay in the village and never leave it after sunset, or like everyone, we shall then live and age and die as all living things do. This is a big decision so I ask you to leave me now and to go and speak of this with your parents as you will outlive them by generations."

Demi did as Fin asked and left him in the glade. She walked slowly back to the cottage her mind full of questions. She was also not at all sure how she was going to speak to Sarah and Mike about all of this.

At the cottage Sarah and Mike were anxiously waiting for Demi to come home. "What if today was too much of a shock for her?" Said Sarah. "Demeter is quite ready to take on her role, I am sure she is up at the glade now talking with Fin. I am also very sure that she would want to accept Fin and that she will be very worried about leaving us. Or us leaving her, especially after your poor health over the past couple of years." Answered Mike. "We need to make this as easy as possible for her. Agreed?" "Agreed." At this Sarah and Mike heard the latch of the cottage door and Demi walked straight into the sitting room her face pale, Sarah and Mike could see that she had been crying. Sarah went to her and put her arms around Demi. "A bit of a full on day today?" Asked Sarah. Demi nodded unable to speak. Mike put a mug of steaming coffee into Demi's hands and waited until she seemed calmer before speaking. "Both your Mother and I know that today has been quite a shock and we also know that you will have met with Fin and he will have told you that you are the Chosen One. We also know that this will be a massive decision for you to make. We shall make it easy for you. If you decide to stay we will not stand in your way. We have also, already, in preparation for this day made our own plans to move either to the village or very close by. Close enough for you to be able to visit us within the time frame you will have each day. We know that you cannot leave the village within the hours of darkness or you will once again become mortal."

Sarah and Mike exchanged glances. They could see that already there were some grey streaks in Demi's red hair, they knew what her answer would be. Demi spoke. "I love you both and never want to leave you. I guess mum knows that I am very torn between staying here with Fin and leaving to come home with you both as mum has been so very ill but my heart is embedded in the village. My love for Fin would never wane. If I left here and never returned my heart would break and I would never be quite whole again."

"Then that is settled." Said Mike. Mike went to the window and looked out into the twilight. "There is Fin now." Mike opened the cottage door and called to Fin. Fin walked towards the cottage an anxious look upon his face. As he drew nearer the welcoming smile on Mike's face calmed all of Fin's fears. As Fin walked into the sitting room Demi ran to him and threw her arms around him. Fin turned to Sarah and Mike. "Thank you for allowing Demeter to be my Lady of the Greenwood. I shall keep her safe and treasure her forever."

Sarah and Mike knew that it would indeed be forever.

LUGHNASADH
POEM

Golden ears of wheat and barley nodding and swaying in the gentle summer breeze.
Golden sunlight reflecting from their burnished seed heads.
Bright red poppies and brilliant blue cornflowers decorate the margins of the fields.

Fruits ripening on trees and hedgerows. A bountiful harvest in a very few weeks. Apples and blackberries for crumbles and pies and cider and wines the winter chill to repel. Green beans on the wigwams of canes and tomatoes on the vine.

Bright orange calendula, red roses and multicoloured sweet peas fill our gardens and delight the senses.
Tiny fledglings are now fully grown. Our gardens are no longer filled with bird song each morning now they are only occasional visitors to our bird table and bath.

Sunny days walking and picnicking, memories to store for cooler winter months ahead.
The Sun God in all splendour still strides high in the sky.
The Goddess in all her beauty and bounty is all around.

LUGHNASADH
MEDITATION

Sit quietly where you won't be disturbed. Take a drink to ground yourself when you return. Light a candle or some incense if appropriate. Adjust your clothes and get comfortable.......

Close your eyes and begin to relax............

When you are ready to begin concentrate on your breathing. Take in a deep breath. Breathe in through your nose. Take the breath deep into your body. Breathe out through your mouth. Breathe in through your nose and out through your mouth, once more in through the nose and out through the mouth. Now still concentrating on your breathing begin to breath naturally.........

Imagine a white light flowing from above onto your head and then down your neck and arms. Now it passes down to the base of your spine and to your legs then down to your feet until you are surrounded by light and it connects you to the earth below.

You are sitting at the edge of a beautiful woodland........ You are leaning against the smooth bark of a tree in dappled shade. Look up. The sky is a wonderful clear blue, the sun shining down from above........

Behind you the woodland is a mixture of broadleaved trees, evergreen holly and some fir trees........

As you sit calmly and quietly you feel at peace with yourself and your surroundings.....

Look slightly to the left and see that the wheat has already been harvested, the bales of straw are still in the fields waiting to be collected.....

In front of you is a wide chalky white path, bone dry as it has been baking hard for weeks in the summer sun.....

Get up and begin to walk along the white path towards some fields on your right..... As you approach the first field you notice that the gate is open. You take this as an invitation to enter the field.....

As you walk into the field you gaze in wonder at the golden wheat and the masses of flowers along the field margin. You notice a hawthorn tree by the hedge. It is casting deep shade, go and sit in the shade of the tree. Sit in silence enjoying the peaceful tranquillity of the place......

As you sit you notice a small movement. It is a harvest mouse gently nibbling on one of the ears of wheat, it's tiny paws wrapped around the stem as is it's tail to keep it balanced. As you watch the mouse nibbling the wheat you notice it's cheeks are bulging with food. Is it to store for winter or does she have a brood of babies waiting in a nest?

After a while the mouse slips quietly away, you sit gazing at the flowers around you. Bright red poppies and blue cornflowers, tall yellow sunflowers, dappled daisies all in abundance. Bees buzzing here and there. Suddenly you notice that the wheat is moving with more purpose. As you watch you see the wheat parting slightly and a Brown Hare gently lopes out of the tall wheat her flanks shining in the sunlight, her noble head and long black tipped ears turned towards you.......

The Hare sits quietly nibbling the grasses at the edge of the field, she is aware of your presence but she knows you are no threat.....Sit for sometime in quiet companionship..............
After a while the Hare turns and looks at you. You look deep into her brown eyes and know at once this is the Goddess. ....She may or may not give you a message..........Quietly

the Hare bows her head as you do in your turn……. The Hare turns and slips away into the wheat. You watch until the wheat is no longer moving…………….

You feel calm and relaxed and at one with the Earth……

When you are ready slowly begin count down from five. Move your shoulders and head from side to side as you come back to the room. If you lit a candle when you blow it out send love and healing to those in need and take a moment to reflect upon the season. Take some small sips of water to ground yourself.

Beltaine

A VILLAGE TALE

Welcome, welcome Goddess of May. The first day of Summer we welcome on this day. Sacred Apple and Hawthorn in bloom, long days of Summer soon will be here. Earth, Air, Fire, Water and Spirit our voices we raise as we welcome you today.

Demi sat staring out of the window of the small cottage she had been sharing with her parents Sarah and Mike. This morning would be the last time she would sit and admire the view of the early morning comings and goings of the village from this room. Today was the day of her wedding or Handfasting to Fin.

Demi had first met Fin a few years ago whilst on holiday with Sarah and Mike. They had met at the Summer Solstice and Demi had almost instantly fallen in love with the enigmatic Fin. It wasn't until a few years later, at the village Lughnasadh ceremony, that Fin had asked Demi to give up her life in the world outside and move to the village to become his Lady of the Land and Harvest. Now a few short months later at Beltaine, Demi and Fin were to make their vows with all of the villagers as witness.

There was a knock at the door and as Demi turned Sarah opened the door and gazed once again at the beautiful green and white gown that hung from a hook on the wall. "You are going to look stunning. Fin is such a lucky guy." Demi smiled. "Yes. It is a beautiful dress and I can't wait to wear it and become Fin's wife." Demi once again felt the overwhelming sense of love she had for Fin and also the slight nervous butterflies that had woken her so early. Hearing voices Mike appeared with a welcome cup of tea accompanied by some hot buttered toast and honey. "For the Bride." Said Mike as he placed the tray on a small table. "Have you both eaten already?" Asked Demi. "Yes the Father and Mother of the Bride need to be up and about early to ensure you haven't changed your mind. Its about time you were off our hands." Laughed Mike. Demi laughed and suddenly realising she was hungry began to tuck into the toast.

The Handfasting ceremony was to take place at ten o'clock before the crowning of the May Queen and the maypole and morris dancing. This would then be followed by a huge feast with more dancing later in the day. The orchard had been prepared ready for the ceremony the previous day. Everyone who was able had helped to set up a small pavilion where the Altar was placed ready to be decorated with flowers and the symbols of the five elements. The pavilion itself was covered in flowers and greenery. The throne had been placed ready upon the large slab of rock that was the centrepiece of the orchard ready for the crowning of the Queen of the May, this too had a large hoop of flowers around it. The apple trees were still covered in pink blossoms and the hawthorn hedges that enclosed the orchard were in full bloom. The whole area had a magical appearance.

The village had been a hive of activity since before dawn as the breads had been baked ready for the feast and pies and other delights were prepared. The actual Handfasting cakes Demi had made herself over the preceding weeks ready to be shared by everyone after the ceremony. The cakes and mead would be blessed during the ceremony itself then all present would eat cake and drink a toast to the newly weds.

After breakfast Demi went out into the cottage garden to pick some flowers for a very small posy for herself and some early roses for her mother and father to wear. The flower headdress that Demi would wear for the ceremony, and the one for the Queen of the May, Demi had made the previous day.

With her flowers picked and arranged Demi prepared for the ceremony. She bathed in a bath of herbs and essential oils and then Sarah helped her into the embroidered gown. At five minutes to ten Demi, Sarah and Mike left the cottage and walked to the orchard. Their way was strewn with flowers that the villagers had placed ready. It seemed the whole village was out lining the way and they began to clap and cheer the wedding party.

After picking up the flowers, the villagers fell in behind Demi and her parents after they had walked past, leading the procession into the orchard where Fin stood waiting near the pavilion with his parents Sweetbriar and Beech. Demi stood a little way off whilst the villagers spaced themselves in a circle around the orchard ready to witness the ceremony. The flowers they had bought with them placed at their feet. A smaller circle was made by Sarah, Mike and the Queen of the May and a few of Demi's close relatives who had come to help celebrate the Handfasting. When everyone was settled Demi and Fin made their way to the south and west of the circle.

"A warm welcome to the Handfasting of our beloved Son Fin and his chosen Lady of the Land and Harvest, Demeter." Announced Beech. As is the custom Sweetbriar and I will conduct the ceremony with the aid of the bride's parents, Sarah and Mike. "Let us begin this sacred ceremony. Before we commence does anyone here present know of any reason why this couple cannot be joined?" A pause for a deep breath by all present and furtive glances around the circle. "No? Then let us begin. Sweetbriar please bless our sacred circle."

Sweetbriar began to close and bless the circle. Then moving

around the circle Sweetbriar welcomed the Guardians of the East, Air. South, Fire. West, Water. North, Earth. Finally Sweetbriar welcomed the Spirit of place by asking if the ceremony may take place on the sacred grounds of the orchard. When the circle was almost complete Sarah walked around the inner circle scattering rose petals upon the ground. The Altar candle was lit and salt and water blessed. Finally the incense burner was lit. Soon the inner circle was filled with wonderful aromas. Beech again blessed the chalice of water and the salt was added to the chalice. Beech then sprinkled the salt water from the chalice around the inside of the smaller circle. "The circle is now cleansed ready for those who are to be joined together to enter." Sarah lead Demi and Fin to the edge of the circle. Beech proclaimed. "Do you wish to be joined together this day and hand fasted as life partners? If this is so enter the sacred circle of your own free will." Demi and Fin entered the circle. Sweetbriar completely closed the circle. Beech took the chalice with the blessed salt water and sprinkled the water at the feet of Demi and Fin. Beech then took up the incense and walked around the inner circle to purify the air. Sweetbriar lead Demi and Fin to the Altar. Fin and Demi each placed the rings that they would exchange into the chalice.

"Demeter. Do you wish to be joined to Fin. Do you make your vows today of free will and of love?" "I do." Replied Demi. "Fin. Do you wish to be joined to Demeter. Do you make your vows today of free will and of love?" "I do." Mike then tied Demi and Fin's hands together with red cord. Sweetbriar said. "As the God and Goddess are bound together I bind you both together as the Lord of the Wildwood and the Lady of the Land and Harvest. To watch over and guide our Village until you deem it time to hand over it's guardianship to your Son."

Sweetbriar and Beech lead Demi and Fin to the Eastern

area of the circle. Beech raised his staff and said. "May you be joined together in love and harmony. May the time you have together be blessed by fair winds that bring you joy in your life for as long as you may live."

Sweetbriar and Beech lead Demi and Fin to the Southern area of the circle. Again Beech raised his staff. "May the Sun warm you in the summer and the fireside keep you from the deep chills of winter. As you journey through your life together may you be blessed with warm hearts filled with love."

Sweetbriar and Beech lead Demi and Fin to the Western area of the circle. "May the gentle waters of our Sacred Glade bless you both. May you ride out any great waves and turbulent times during your life together so that you may live in harmony."

Then Sweetbriar and Beech guided Demi and Fin to the Northern area of the circle. "As you continue your life together upon the sacred Earth may you find comfort in one another as you keep the sacred rite. May you help and guide one another during times of troubles when the tears may flow. May you spend your time together planting the seeds of the future."

Lastly Sweetbriar and Beech lead Demi and Fin to the Altar. For the final time Beech raised his staff. "Demeter and Fin. May the wisdom of the God and Goddess guide you on your journey through life together. May you walk a sacred path and share delight in one another. May you remain soul mates and best friends for as long as your time upon the Earth may last. May you grow old and wiser together. May your union be blessed with a child to carry forward the great works that you undertake willingly to support our Village. May you share all things in times of joy and of great sadness. May you share joy and love."

Sweetbriar removed the rings from the chalice. "Now place these rings upon one another's finger's and make your own private vows of love." Demi placed her ring to Fin upon his finger then Fin placed his ring to Demi upon her finger. They didn't need to say anything as their eyes met and mutual love, affection and longing was plain for all to see.

Sweetbriar asked them. "As you are now bound and beringed are you ready for your final vows?"

"Yes." Said Demi and Fin in unison. Sweetbriar turned to Demi. "Demeter. Before the Goddess and the God do you take Fin to be your sworn partner. Will you be faithful, caring, loving and nurturing? Do you keep this promise for as long as your love shall last?" "I will." Replied Demi.

Sweetbriar then turned to Fin. "Fin. Before the Goddess and the God do you take Demeter to be your sworn partner. Will you be faithful, caring, loving and nurturing? Do you keep this promise for as long as your love shall last?" "I will." Replied Fin.

"Now is the time for you to leap into the future." Said Beech. Sarah and Mike bought forward the broom and held it raised from the ground in front of Demi and Fin. Laughing Demi and Fin leapt into the air as high as they could over the broom. "Now go into your future together. May you be happy all of your days. Blessed Be."

Everyone began to cheer and ring the hand bells they had bought with them.

Sweetbriar raised her hands in the air and all became silent. "I now bless the cake and mead that was given to you as you arrived here today. I bless the cake and the mead that we have on our Altar. As you eat and drink today make a small offering to the God and Goddess and the Spirit of the Place. So Mote it Be."

Mike raised his voice so all may hear. "Now Demi and Fin shall cut the cake that we have here. You already have your cake and mead as given to you when you arrived. When the cake is cut all present drink a toast to Demeter and Fin and enjoy your cake."

Demi and Fin cut their cake and passed it around to those in the smaller circle. Mead was poured. When all was ready Mike raised his glass. "To Demeter and Fin. Long and happy life. Blessed Be."

"To Demeter and Fin. Long and happy life. Blessed Be." Rang out around the orchard. The bells rang out again and everyone clapped and cheered. Fin spoke. "Thank you all for coming today to wish us well upon our future journey through life together. Demi and I will try to take turns to speak to you all after the feast later today. But now it is time for the really important celebration of the day we must crown our May Queen." Everyone laughed.

Sarah and Mike lead the May Queen forward. Demi held out her hand. "Come climb upon the Orchard Stone to be crowned Queen of the May." Demi and the Queen climbed upon the stone and Demi lead the child to the May Throne. "I crown you Queen of the May. May the God and Goddess bless you for today and for all of your tomorrows. Blessed Be." Demi placed the circlet of flowers upon the child's head and the crowd cheered and clapped yet again. Fin joined Demi on the Stone. "Now let the Maypole and Morris Dancing begin."

The village children began to gather around the Maypole and to pick up the brightly coloured ribbons and as the dancing began they chanted:

"Welcome, welcome Goddess of May. The first day of Summer we welcome on this day. Sacred Apple and Hawthorn in bloom, long days of Summer soon will be here. Earth, Air, Fire, Water and Spirit our voices we raise as we welcome you today."

Whilst the children were dancing around the Maypole the Morris Men played and danced on the village green. The

"Obby Oss" pretended to chase the young girls who ran away screeching with delight.

Families sat picnicking in the orchard and on the green. The day passed with much fun and merriment. Finally, as the Sun began to set, everyone who was able gathered in the village hall for the traditional May day feast. The feast was extra special this year as it was also a feast to celebrate Demi and Fin's Handfasting. Some would miss the feast, as by now, they were sleeping under the trees in the orchard or woodlands much the worse for the mead, cider and ales.

Towards the end of the evening just as the sun was beginning to set Fin caught Demi's eye. Demi nodded. Quietly they slipped away from the hall hand in hand. They made their way to the cottage at the edge of the village that they would now share. They went to the back garden and sat side by side to watch the sunset. Fin had bought some mead and cake with him. When their glasses were full Demi and Fin raised the glasses, "To us and our future together." They sipped the sweet honey wine and nibbled cake before making their way indoors.

BLESSED BELTAINE

Snowy white Mayflowers adorn the Hawthorn. Tree of the Goddess we revere you. The Green Man wonders the virgin woodlands from dawn 'til dusk.

Bright green leaves unfurling in the hedgerows and woodlands. Will it be Oak or Ash first to appear heralding a "Splash or a Soak" in the coming months.

The Ransomes are now fully emerged from their Winter slumber, bright green shoots reach for the sky, their wonderful aroma fills the air.

Bluebells beginning to bloom amongst the fallen fronds of last summer's bracken. Maypole dancing, the phallic symbol of old. Courting couples chasing all night in the woodlands and fields.

The God and Goddess now seal their union, the Earth Mother now showing she is in full bloom. Longer days filled with the promise of summer.

Blessed Beltaine

BELTAINE
MEDITATION

Sit quietly where you won't be disturbed. Take a drink to ground yourself when you return. Light a candle or some incense if appropriate. Adjust your clothes and get comfortable…….

Close your eyes and begin to relax………….

When you are ready to begin concentrate on your breathing. Take in a deep breath. Breathe in through your nose. Take the breath deep into your body. Breathe out through your mouth. Breathe in through your nose and out through your mouth, once more in through the nose and out through the mouth. Now still concentrating on your breathing begin to breath naturally………..

You are walking through a deciduous woodland. New growth and life is all around you, see the new leaves on the trees, wild garlic and bluebells………. When you look up the sky is a wonderful blue and the sun is shining through the trees making dappled patterns on the woodland floor……….. All around you there is calm and the only sound is the birdsong that fills the air. Robin, blackbird, wren and countless others all busy finding food to feed their ever demanding broods…….

The air is filled with the perfume of the Bluebells that cover the woodland floor.

After a while you reach a clearing. The sun is shining into the clearing and you decide to sit under the shade of an old Oak tree. The tree trunk is gnarled and the ground beneath you is covered with the fallen leaves of last Autumn. You sit with your back to the tree feeling calm and relaxed…….

You look around the clearing and notice that it is almost a

complete circle, all of the trees in this area are oaks of various ages. Their leaves are almost all unfurled and are a lovely pale, almost lime green and the tips are tinged a copper colour.

A movement catches your eye and you turn to look to your left. A beautiful silver grey horse appears in the clearing, he sees you and walks across to where you are sitting. He bends his head and nuzzles your neck, you feel his warm breath on your neck and cheek. You reach up and stroke his velvety soft muzzle. After a while the horse moves off to your right and lies down contentedly...........

Look across the clearing and notice that rabbits have now appeared and are happily nibbling the grass. A wren flies towards the horse and perches on it's flank.

Soon many woodland animals appear. Fox, badger and deer all come into the clearing to either graze or sit quietly. The rabbits are unconcerned about the fox as he is not hunting, all of the creatures know you are there but are happy to share the space with you......

Finally a Hare appears and sits watching to the left, the direction she came from............

Suddenly all of the creatures stop what they are doing and look to the left of the clearing. You know they have heard something or someone approaching............

A pure white Stallion appears being lead by a tall man dressed in green, his hair curls around his shoulders, he has a garland of Ivy upon his head. As you gaze in wonder you see the Lady upon the horse. She is dressed in green and white with a garland of flowers in her long flowing red hair. You know that this is The Goddess and her Lord of the Greenwood. The God lifts the Goddess to the ground. The wren flies to perch upon her shoulder and the Hare greets the Lady......

All of the woodland creatures bow their heads in reverence,

as do you. The Lady walks around the clearing stopping to bless each creature as she passes, she is followed by the Lord and the Hare. When she comes to you she stops and stands quietly. She may give you a message to take away from this sacred space…………..

Finally the Lady completes her circle and returns to the Stallion, the Lord lifts her onto the horse and then silently the Lady and her Lord leave the clearing. After a while all of the creatures begin to leave. You stand and give thanks to this sacred space and then turn and walk back along the path in the direction you came from…………..

When you are ready slowly begin count down from five. Move your shoulders and head from side to side as you come back to the room. If you lit a candle when you blow it out send love and healing to those in need and take a moment to reflect upon the season. Take some small sips of water to ground yourself.

EARLY MORNING WALK ON THE LEVELS

Baby Rabbits play in misty dewy grass, carefree days of freedom and frolics,
Hares browsing in newly mown fields are suddenly startled by a small brown dog, swiftly they run along a sun baked farm track, the small dog strains at the leash, this is a game she would love.

Foxes hunting for voles and shrews amongst clumps of grass. They stop the hunt to look and stare at us as we watch them and marvel at their beauty.
Suddenly they break cover and run for the hedge.
Birdsong loud on the early morning air. In the distance a Cuckoo is calling.

Trees are in full leaf providing shade for grateful animals and birds.
Elder flowers perfume the air, hay fever sneezes soon follow.
Cow parsley, wild carrot and angelica fill the verges. Reeds and flag iris fill the rhynes, the banks lined with withies.

Cattle graze the fields, hooves obscured by early morning mist.
Overhead a buzzard mews during his early morning hunt.
We turn back to begin the walk home,
Tea, coffee and second breakfast awaits.

We live very near to the Somerset Levels. A rhyne is a drainage ditch. Withies are the local name for willow trees.

Imbolc

A VILLAGE TALE

"*On my journey through the eternal Wheel of life shall you be by my side. Maiden, Mother and Crone. As I am reborn each Lughnasadh so shall your beauty be restored at Imbolc. In March at Ostara we shall become one. At Beltaine we shall celebrate as the Lord and Lady of the Greenwood. At Litha you shall be blooming whilst I hold full power over the length of days. At Lughnasadh you shall raise me. At Mabon your harvest will be fullsome, the Cornucopia of bounty forthcoming. At Samhain the Wild Hunt I shall lead, by now a Crone you shall be. At Yule we shall witness the rebirth of the Sun God for that is the way of the Wheel.*"

It was early morning in the village. The biting frost of last night was still white upon the ground. The apple trees in the orchard were covered, as though a thin layer of snow had fallen. Dragon's breath filled the air as the Crone shuffled and stumbled her way through the orchard towards the Glade. She shivered and pulled her cloak closer around her bowed shoulders. A mane of white hair escaping from the hood and hiding her face. As she reached the top of the orchard she opened the gate and began the painful climb over the boulders towards the Glade, stopping every so often her breath forming misty clouds of vapour. The journey, as ever, having almost used all of her strength.

She was almost there now she could hear the rushing of the winter waters through the Glade. Gone the soft trickle of the stream of summer days. The stream was angry and full of the melting snow waters from the high moors above. The Crone stopped, stunned as ever even after all this time by the beauty of this sacred space. Slowly, carefully, reverently she knelt down on the edge of the rock pool where the stream eddied and flowed more slowly. She cupped her hands and drank the icy cold waters and then bathed her face and hands. As she did so she could already feel her vitality and strength beginning to return and as she looked her hands began to regain their youthful beauty. She gazed at her reflection in the water. Youthful eyes stared back at her from a face framed once more by a mane of red hair.

It had happened once again. The Crone was gone for another year and the Maiden now knelt in her place. Demi felt that she would never understand the mysteries of her magickal transformation at each Imbolc.

It was several years now since Demi had met Fin, the magickal Lord of the Wildwood, who had captivated her the first time they had met at the Summer Solstice. Then a few years later the experiences at Lughnasadh had sealed their relationship and Demi had agreed to stay in the Village as the Lady of the Land and Harvest to Her Lord of the Wildwood. Demi heard a soft sound behind her, she turned and smiled. "It's done then?" Fin stood there smiling. As ever Demi's heart melted and she rushed to his embrace. "Yes I am once more restored."

Hand in hand they gave thanks to the Spirit of Place and of Water and then left the Glade heading to the small cottage on the edge of the Village that they had shared since their Hand fasting several years ago.

Their way home took them back through the village orchard, the scene of all the festivals and festivities throughout the year. The apple trees were still covered in the ribbons and clouties placed there by the families of the village at the annual wassailing ceremony at the old Twelfth Night celebrations two weeks ago. The whole village had come for the ceremony. The weather was perfect, cool and crisp, the Moon's fullness illuminating the orchard. It was a village tradition that each family had their own tree. They tended it and cared for it the whole year carrying out any pruning needed and checking it for any signs of disease. At the Wassailing ceremony the families stood next to their tree and banged drums or pots and pans or shouted to scare away any bad spirits. In the centre of the orchard three shotguns were fired into the air to keep away any spirits who hadn't quite got the message. Then the chosen Wassail Queen and King were lifted up to place toast that had been soaked in cider into the branches of the very central tree and then poured a libation of cider onto the roots. Whilst this was happening all present sang the Wassail song;

Here's to thee old apple tree, much fruit mayest though bear, hats full, caps full and great bushel baskets full, and some for under the stairs. Hurrah!

Then all the villagers placed toast that had been soaked in cider into the branches of their tree and poured a libation onto the roots. Ribbons were tied onto the lower branches to offer blessings and thanks for the trees. Afterwards everyone stood around drinking mulled cider or apple juice and enjoying a supper of crusty bread, cheese and pickles. Wassailing was a time for families and friends to get together at a time of the year that can be very dark and lonely. When the long days of summer seem so very far away, it was a ceremony enjoyed by all. It was a ceremony that was organised by the villagers, one that Demi and Fin did not lead. They went along for the fun and festivities and the supper.

Since that day of the Lughnasadh festival, several years ago, many things had happened. Mike and Sarah, Demi's parents had moved to the village to be close to their only child. Demi upon becoming Fin's consort was unable to leave the village for no more than a few hours or she would become mortal once more. Demi knew that at some point in the future that both she and Fin would leave the village and live out the rest of their lives as mortal folk. That would not be until they had raised a son of their own, who in time would become the Lord of the Wildwood. Their work would then be done and they could leave a successor and protector of the Village for the future. Demi knew that this would not be for many years.

"Look." Said Fin, "The first Snowdrops are out." Demi looked and yes as ever on the day of her rebirth the icy frost had disappeared and several clumps of Snowdrops were now in bloom. As they walked through the Village more and more Snowdrops appeared, Demi knew that this would be the sign for the people who lived in the Village, both incomers and those families who had lived in the village for generations, that Spring was indeed returning and the Lady of the Land and Harvest was returned to them once more.

This transformation had been happening for several years now. Demi was always at a loss to understand how the magick worked. She knew that as long as she stayed in the village and by Fin's side it would happen year upon year until the new Lord of the Greenwood was conceived and born, grew to adulthood, and would then take on the mantle.

Not long after Demi had agreed to stay with Fin he had taken her to see Someone Very Special as he had phrased it. They had left the Village very early on a beautiful sunny morning in early February several weeks before their Handfasting. They had climbed up onto the moors close by, leaving the boundary of the Village, until they came to the edge of a small hamlet. A mist of smoke came from the chimney set in the thatched roof. The front door was open and as they approached an elderly man opened the door wide. Fin embraced the old man warmly. "Come in, come in, Ma is in the back." Demi and Fin followed the rather stooped elderly man into the cottage which was dark inside after the bright sun lit day outside. When they reached a small kitchen they saw a white haired lady sitting in a rocking chair next to a range. As they approached she stood up slowly to embrace Fin and then Demi. "So let me look at you my dear, we are so thrilled to be meeting you at last. We have heard so much about you. Oh Fin, you have not done her justice, she is indeed the most beautiful girl I have ever seen." Demi could feel herself blushing rather unbecomingly. "Oh come along my dear don't be shy, we welcome you to our family."

Demi thought that at last she understood, this must be Fin's grandparents. "It is wonderful to meet you, Fin has been very coy about mentioning any family…..." Demi was just about to say it was lovely to meet Fin's grandparents when the elderly lady carried on. "As Fin's Mother and Father we are so happy that at long last he has found the right partner to be by his side. As you must realise we are both now very elderly and will not be upon the Earth for much longer. Soon it will be time for us to take the Great Journey and we shall be no more upon this Land."

Demi had to work very hard to not gasp in amazement. These two very elderly people were Fin's parents? But of course. The realisation hit Demi like a blow. Fin had immortality if he stayed within the boundaries of the Village between sunset and sunrise. To leave the Village after sunset or to stay away from the Village meant that Fin would then age like any other mortal, as would Demi, now she had agreed to become Lady of the Land and Harvest.

Fin's Father, Beech, was speaking now. "I can see what you are thinking, how will you age when your time in the Village is done and you and Fin leave after raising a son to be the new Lord of the Wildwood? Well my Daughter, you will age at the normal rate, you will not suddenly grow old as you do at the moment, your beauty restored at Imbolc as the Wheel turns. You and Fin will leave the Village when the time feels right for you both. Our cottage will be here for you as it has stood for all the generations of our family." "So how long ago did you leave the Village?" Asked Demi. "Oh we left a little over fifty years ago." Sweetbriar, Fin's Mother answered with a smile. "As you can see we have aged together and when our time comes we shall cross the Bridge together too, being seen safely across by the Lord of the Wildhunt." Demi knew by now that at Samhain Fin became the Lord of the Wildhunt. "So Fin shall see you safely across when your time comes?" "Yes as in turn many, many years from now your Son shall show you both across together for that is the way of things." Demi was relieved by this for she had worried about how she would cope without Fin when she became old. Demi had known when she agreed to stay with Fin that she would not age as a mortal. She would have to watch her own parent's Sarah and Mike age and then die and she would be left with no other family.

The rest of the day passed full of fun and laughter. Demi felt so comfortable and at home she was almost reluctant to leave Sweetbriar and Beech to return to the Village with Fin. Demi hoped that there would be many other visits in the future. "Now you come up and visit us any time my dear now Fin has shown you the way. No need to be asked or wait for Fin to bring you." Demi nodded and smiled her thanks as she set off with Fin.

"Oh what lovely people Sweetbriar and Beech are, why haven't I met them before?" Asked Demi. "Well because I had to be sure that you would have me and accept all the responsibility of what the Village expects of us both."

A few weeks later at Beltaine, Demi and Fin were Handfasted in the Village orchard, the focal point of Village life for hundreds of years. The ceremony was lead by Sweetbriar and Beech as was the traditional custom. After the ceremony Fin and Demi crowned the Queen of the May whose throne was placed upon the large slab of rock in the orchard, which, for many years now had the names of the May Queens carved into the rock. After the ceremonies much feasting and merriment had followed until exhausted, everyone began to drift home. A few, who didn't make it home, slept under the trees in the orchard waking the following day with some very sore heads indeed. Of course some of them had been up all Beltaine Eve following the old traditions in the surrounding woodlands. Many pairings were sealed and Handfastings already being planned.

Demi and Fin left for their cottage on the outskirts of the village as the festivities were beginning to die down, their own tradition to fulfil.

That had all happened several years ago. The Wheel had turned many times since that memorable day of commitment, sunshine, maypole dancing and merriment. Demi and Fin lived a quiet life in the Village. Fin busily keeping the cottage maintained and helping out the older villagers with gardening. Demi tended the cottage garden growing vegetables and fruits for her and Fin and giving away any surplus to the less fortunate.

The Wheel continued to turn with Fin and Demi leading the rituals and ceremonies. Baby namings, Handfastings and the rite of Samhain at Summer's end when Fin lead the spirits of those departed across the Bridge to the Summerlands beyond.

SNOWMAIDS

Brave Snowmaids first to appear, long have we looked for you, at last you are here, Grey/green spikes bravely push through the cold damp Earth.

The nights still freeze and threaten snow but still you greet each new dawn. Delicate white flowers nod in the harsh winter winds.

Today our Goddess Brighid returns to us as the Maiden. She awaits her Green Lord in the Spring at Ostara.

We rejoice as the days begin to grow longer. The birds are beginning to sing once again. We await the return of warmer Spring days.

Lambs gambolling in the fields, rushing back to ewes to drink, tales wagging happily. New grass beginning to grow as the daylight lengthens.

Rivers and streams overflowing with rains and melted snows will wash the snowmaid's bulbs far and wide.

Our spirits are lifted by the crisp clear air as we walk the foot paths, hedgerows and fields. Already buds are set upon the trees waiting to burst forth when the days are warmer,

Lambs tail catkins sway in the breeze. Pussy Willow delight the eyes, young children love to stroke their soft downy sides. Already in sheltered spots the primroses are beginning to grow.

Signs of new growth are all around for those who take the time to look for Gaia's wonderful gifts. Blessed Imbolc.

IMBOLC
MEDITATION

Sit quietly where you won't be disturbed. Take a drink to ground yourself when you return. Light a candle or some incense if appropriate. Adjust your clothes and get comfortable.......

Close your eyes and begin to relax.............

When you are ready to begin concentrate on your breathing. Take in a deep breath. Breathe in through your nose. Take the breath deep into your body. Breathe out through your mouth. Breathe in through your nose and out through your mouth, once more in through the nose and out through the mouth. Now still concentrating on your breathing begin to breath naturally.........

You are in ancient woodland. It is very early in the morning. There is no one else around.

The trees are bare of leaves as this is the very beginning of spring, this is Imbolc the feast of Brighid............

Look up at the sky. The light is beginning build towards the east. Look behind you to the west and there it is still dark and some stars are just visible........... The moon set a while ago...........Begin to walk towards the light through the woodland.......... As you walk you see a stream to your right, it is in full flow, the winter rains and snow from the hills has melted and flowed down into the valley.

As the light levels build you see millions of snowdrops everywhere, at your feet and way into the distance...........

As you walk you see the ancient trees their bark covered in rich green mosses and small ferns, you reach out and touch the moss, it is soft, springy and warm…………...

Follow the path walking slowly. Wonder at the display of snowdrops, their white flowers tipped with green…………...

The path comes to a bridge. Step onto the bridge and stop. Look at the stream flowing towards you then turn to watch as it flow away into the distance………. Take the opportunity to banish any negative thoughts and worries into the water. As the stream flows away from you so do your worries…………….

Now continue to walk along the path heading ever towards the building daylight…………... The path begins to climb upwards. It is a gentle slope not a steep climb………………

As you walk you begin to hear the birds sing, the sound of the running water had masked the early morning chorus, now you hear it strong and clear…………...

After a while you reach the top of the woodland……….. Pause and look back at the flowers in the valley below. From here a white carpet of snowdrops covers the valley floor…………...

Go through a small gate and out into a meadow……….. As you reach the top of the meadow the sun breaks over the horizon in all it's early morning glory of silver, yellow and orange…….. Raise your arms in greeting to the risen sun and the new day…………….You feel at one with nature and at peace………...

When you are ready slowly begin count down from five. Move your shoulders and head from side to side as you come back to the room. If you lit a candle when you blow it out send love and healing to those in need and take a moment to reflect upon the season. Take some small sips of water to ground yourself.

Ostara

A VILLAGE TALE

The Spring equinox dawned clear and bright. The full moon still hung in the sky as the rising sun turned the sky from milky white to soft orange and then to flaming red as the sun burst over the horizon.

Demi and Fin made their way back towards the centre of the Village. They had watched the Sunrise from their favourite place at the very top of the hill that overlooked the Village and the moors in the distance. They had spent last night alone together in the Glade.

Later in the orchard there would be painted egg hunts. When the eggs were found they could be exchanged for chocolate eggs to enjoy later at the feast. Egg rolling and running races, including of course an egg and spoon race and pancake races. There was also mulled cider or apple juice and hot cross buns for all.

Ostara, is a traditional time for family gatherings. Often the first since Yule. It is a time of feasting and to welcome the return of Spring. It is a time of fun and festivities, the time of birth of later lambs and warmer longer days. It was a time of Equinox. The time when daylight and darkness were of equal length. After this day the daylight would return and the darkness would gradually disappear until the Autumn equinox or Mabon. It was a festival that Demi loved. This year was going to be an extra special festival for Ostara. Demi and Fin had decided it was time their new Son would be conceived for the birth of the new Sun God and Lord of the Wildwood at Yule.

It was now many years since Demi had come to the Village with her parents Sarah and Mike for a holiday and to join in the Summer Solstice celebrations. The time when Demi and Fin had first met and had fallen almost instantly in love. Sarah and Mike were now in their older years and Demi very much wanted them to have some time with a Grandson before they passed over the rainbow bridge. Fin was in complete agreement. He had been Lord of the Wildwood and custodian of the Village for several generations and he felt it was time to pass on the title to his Son. The moon would also be waxing to fullness at Yule when their Son would be born.

Fin was already dressed in his guise of the Green Man and Demi was wearing her green gown. Fin left to wander in the woods whilst Demi joined several other villagers to collect the painted eggs for hiding. The eggs were duly hidden in and around the orchard and also around the village green. There should be at least one egg for each child in the Village, but in case a child was disappointed there were always many more chocolate eggs than hidden painted ones, plus more eggs to give out as prizes for the races.

Promptly at ten o'clock everyone began to gather in the orchard ready for the festivities to begin. The Morris Men were playing folk songs whilst everyone was arriving. As the village clock struck ten o'clock Demi and Fin climbed onto the large rock in the orchard, the crowd fell silent. "Welcome all." Said Fin. "Welcome to our Ostara celebrations, the eggs are hidden and the races will begin at eleven o'clock. Now is the time for all children, young and old to search for eggs. Drum roll please." One of the Morris Men began to beat his drum. At this all of the children sped off around the orchard and village green in search of the hidden eggs.

The Morris Men began to play and dance and several of the villagers lead by Demi and Fin began to join in. Soon the first children arrived back to the rock to claim their chocolate eggs in exchange for the painted eggs they had found. Before the eggs had been hidden they had been counted so that it would be known when all the eggs had been found. Inevitably some children found more than one egg and some found none, the spare eggs were given out so no child was disappointed.

Next it was time for the races to begin. First it was the egg and spoon races with the usual lost eggs and tripping over, amid much laughter and merriment. These were followed by the egg rolling and lastly the pancake races. The pancake races were last so that more pancakes could be cooked on the griddles set up in the orchard. Everyone had pancakes with a choice of filling for a late lunch, if room of course after the chocolate eggs and hot cross buns.

By now some of the adults were feeling slightly merry after consuming several pints of cider so the morris dancing was becoming slightly raucous and disorganised.

Demi took some of the children to one side and began to tell one of their favourite stories.

THE GODDESS AND THE HARE

A very long time ago, the Goddess Eostre was out walking in the forest and she found an injured bird. The Goddess was unable to heal the bird and so transformed it into a Hare. Whilst the Goddess was performing her spell she was distracted and something went wrong and the transformation was not quite complete so the Hare/bird retained the ability to lay eggs. Each year at the Goddess' festival, to show it's appreciation to the Goddess for saving it's life, the Hare laid some eggs and left them as an offering for the Goddess.

Some of the younger children fell asleep after all of the excitement so Demi sang some songs quietly. The other older children went to play games in amongst the trees until it was time for the evening feast and prize giving.

"Hello, I thought I may find you here." It was Sarah, Demi's mother. Demi smiled and gave Sarah a hug. "Yes. It is a tiring day for the little ones, up early and then all of the rushing around to find eggs and the games." Sarah looked at the sleeping children, a look of sadness in her eyes. Both Sarah and Mike had really hoped to see their Grandson before they died. Demi caught the look. "Don't worry Mum, there will be some news very soon." Sarah started. "You mean?" The question hung in the air. Demi's smile was enough to answer Sarah's question. "Oh, I am so pleased for you both and your Father will be over the moon. I must find him and tell him the news." "No wait. I must find Fin and we shall tell him together. But we must wait for these little ones to wake first. I promised I wouldn't leave them alone whilst their parents are helping to set up the feast in the hall."

Sarah sat quietly with Demi as they watched over the sleeping children. One by one the children began to wake and their parents fetched them in readiness for the evening feasting.

When the last child had been collected Demi saw Fin in the distance. Fin saw Demi wave and began to walk across to where Demi and Sarah stood. On his way Fin spoke to Mike and they both walked over to where Demi and Sarah were waiting. "Lovely day as ever." Said Mike. "Well organised. I think everyone has had a wonderful time and judging by the chocolatey faces of the children I think all of the eggs must have been found. I shall never tire of living in the Village." Fin looked at Sarah. Immediately he realised that Demi had told her the news. "We have some news for you both." Began Fin. Sarah broke into a massive grin, tears of joy forming. Mike looked at Sarah and then at Fin and Demi. "Is the news what I think it may be?" Mike also broke into a massive grin. "Yes, our Son was conceived last night to be born at Yule." Replied Fin. "Now you must keep this to yourselves until we make an announcement at the prize giving later." Sarah and Mike hugged Demi and Fin and then one another. "Yes of course we shall keep the news quiet until later. Massive congratulations from us both." Said Sarah.

Later at the evening feast Sarah and Mike could barely keep the smiles from their faces and they kept stealing glances across the hall to where Demi and Fin sat. Some of the more astute older women realised very quickly what was going on and the whispered news spread amongst them like a breeze through ripe barley. When everyone had almost finished eating Fin stood and the room became very quiet. "Now is the time for the prize giving before the younger folks start to nod off." At this someone shouted, "And before some of the Old Codgers who have had too much cider." Everyone laughed and Fin nodded his agreement. "And that too." The prizes were announced by Fin and Demi handed them out, accompanied by much cheering and laughter not to mention some ribald comments from some of the more merry villagers. After the prize giving some chocolate eggs were left over so Fin and Demi turned their backs to the hall and threw the eggs over their shoulders as far as they could into the crowd for the villagers to catch.

After the eggs had all gone. Fin and Demi turned again to face the room. By now Sarah and Mike were almost bursting to share the news of Demi's pregnancy and some of the older women began nudging one another in the ribs and whispering. Fin waited until a hush had fallen over the room once more. "Demi and I have some news to share with you all." Most of the women now broke into broad grins and could barely stop from cheering. "A new infant of the Wildwood will be born at Yule." Sarah and Mike began to cheer but this was soon drowned out by the clapping and cheering from everyone assembled. Everyone began to congratulate Demi and Fin and of course Sarah and Mike. Glasses were quickly refilled to drink a toast to Demi and Fin and Sarah and Mike.

The Morris Men began to play once again and the evening passed with more dancing and celebration.

GODDESS MOON

Silent, mysterious. Our Goddess Moon.
Gently each month you are born.
Slowly you grow from nothing to fullness and then quietly
wane and die.
We too are born Maiden, become Mother, and then slowly
fade to become Crone.

As you wax to fullness the Hare is revealed.
On the Earth Hares dance by your silvery light.
Forms are abandoned as the gaze transfixed.
Around standing stones, in fields and hilltops they dance the
night away.

Silent, silver Goddess Moon.
Our lives, moods and tides you govern.
We plant our seeds as you wax and grow.
Our crops we reap under your full harvest light.

OSTARA
MEDITATION

Sit quietly where you won't be disturbed. Take a drink to ground yourself when you return. Light a candle or some incense if appropriate. Adjust your clothes and get comfortable.......

Close your eyes and begin to relax..............

When you are ready to begin concentrate on your breathing. Take in a deep breath. Breathe in through your nose. Take the breath deep into your body. Breathe out through your mouth. Breathe in through your nose and out through your mouth, once more in through the nose and out through the mouth. Now still concentrating on your breathing begin to breath naturally..........

You are sitting on a stone in the centre of a stone circle. The Sun has just risen and the sky is a wonderful blue shot with warm orange, gold and silver. Welcome the dawn and give thanks to the Goddess and the God..............

As you look down into the valley below there are still some patches of overnight mist, it seems as though you are floating above the land............

You are feeling relaxed and at peace...... Feel the energy of the Sun on your head and then feel it as it travels down your body to connect you to the Earth...... Turn around and look at the view......The fir tree topped hills in the distance. The rocky crags. The valley is now bathed in sunlight the mist has evaporated as the sun rises ever higher.

Feel the warmth of the sun on your neck, shoulders and head massaging away any tension, stress and aches......

Remove your shoes and socks and feel your feet connecting with the Earth. Look down and see green blades of grass between your toes. Walk to one of the upright stones. Stand with your back to the stone….. Feel the warmth of the stone and the energy of the stone. You feel alive, vital and refreshed ready to face whatever the day may bring…..

Send healing thoughts to those whom you know are in need……

Listen to the birdsong and the gentle buzz of the bees in the gorse beyond the stone circle and those who are closer on the soft herbs near your feet……

Take time to relax in this calm space ………….

When you are ready to leave, slowly begin count down from five. Move your shoulders and head from side to side as you come back to the room. If you lit a candle when you blow it out send love and healing to those in need and take a moment to reflect upon the season. Take some small sips of water to ground yourself.

I was inspired to write this after a very early morning visit to Mitchell's Fold stone circle, Shropshire

Mabon

A VILLAGE TALE

Thanks be to our bountiful trees. Much fruit hast though borne.

Goddess of the Earth we honour you today.

We give thanks to the elements of Earth, Air, Fire, Water and Spirit.

Fertile Earth. Cool clean Air. Warm fiery Sun, to heat the land our crops to bear. Pure clear Waters to quench the land.

Ever enduring Spirit of the soul and the Spirit of our sacred spaces. Blessed Be

The Wheel had turned once more. Before anyone had really noticed, it was the time for the apple harvest. The trees in the village orchard were almost bent double by the bumper crop once again this year.

Notices began to appear in the Village asking for help with the harvest. The traditional date of 22nd September was set and the times were between Bat roost and Bat rise, or Sunrise and Sunset. A busy twelve hours of labour followed by an end of harvest supper of breads and cheeses and apple pies and cider to wash it all down with.

All of the villagers helped, from the younger children to the older villagers who were still spry enough to bend. Those that were not able to help with the harvest looked after the babes in arms and toddlers and prepared the harvest feast.

As ever, before the first apples were picked from the trees on harvest day proper, some of the windfall apples had already been cleared to use for chutneys and pies for the feast. Nothing was ever wasted, any apples left over were used for their juice.

At sunrise everyone was ready assembled in the orchard. Fin, accompanied Demi, as The Lady of the Land and Harvest climbed up onto the large slab of stone in the orchard.

Demi spoke. "As the Lady of the Land and Harvest I declare that this harvest should begin. May the blessings of the Goddess Gaia be upon you all. We hope for a bumper harvest to sustain us through the lean times of winter ahead. Blessed Be." Everyone cheered. As Demi had turned to give her Blessing it was plain for all to see her beauty and her blooming pregnancy. The villagers knew that the future of the Village would be secured when the new Lord of the Wildwood was born at Yule.

Those who were to prepare the food for the supper left the orchard. Demi accompanied them to begin the mammoth task of baking the many loaves for the feasting much later in the day. Everyone else began the task in hand. Ladders were placed at the base of the trees and the apples carefully picked, those apples that fell to the ground and may be bruised were placed in separate bags to be used first. Everyone worked hard all day with barely a short break for lunch.

At last, as the sun began to set, the last apples were picked and a great whoop of joy went up from all of the harvesters. Demi and Fin climbed up once again onto the giant boulder in the orchard. "Many blessings and thanks to everyone who has helped this day. The harvesters and those who have laboured in the kitchens to prepare our harvest feast. We give thanks to all. Blessed Be."

Demi and Fin then lead everyone to the village green where a huge feast had been laid out. Those who had spent the day gathering the harvest were first to be served. After supper the Morris Men began to play and dance, many of the villagers joined in with the dancing and singing.

The next morning it was time for the apples to be sorted. Some were put into storage for the long winter months ahead. Those apples that were very bruised were set aside for juicing and cider making and some were given out to the villagers to make chutneys for the feasts throughout the year.

Later in the day Demi and Fin lead the ceremony of thanks to the trees for the apple harvest. The villagers followed Demi and Fin through the orchard chanting and drumming to give thanks to the Goddess, the trees and the five sacred elements.

Thanks be to our bountiful trees. Much fruit hast though borne. Goddess of the Earth we honour you today.

We give thanks to the elements of Earth, Air, Fire, Water and Spirit.

Fertile Earth. Cool clean Air. Warm firey Sun, to heat the land our crops to bear. Pure clear Waters to quench the land.

Ever enduring Spirit of the soul and the Spirit of our sacred spaces. Blessed Be

As the chanting and drumming took place Demi could feel the baby inside her womb kicking in time to the drum beats, as though he already knew his destiny. Demi and Fin shared a secret smile. Soon the new Lord of the Wildwood would be born to carry on the traditions of the Village.

MABON
SECOND HARVEST

Bramble bushes laden with fruit.
Blackberry juice running down my chin, I sample as I pick.
Apple and pear trees. Branches almost toppling under the weight.
Mouthwatering ciders, perrys, pies and crumbles, the taste buds to delight.

Jams made, chutneys and pickles on the boil.
Surplus veg and fruits to bottle and freeze.
Preparing for the long cold lean months ahead.
The Goddess' ripeness and bounty. "The Horn of Plenty" to fill.

Misty early mornings begin with an Autumnal nip in the air.
Our Sun God rises to chase away the mists. His warmth and power are still strong.
Days and nights of equal length. Stories of Demeter and Persephone.
Log stores full ready to combat winter's chills. As we celebrate the Wheel ever turns.

MABON
MEDITATION

Sit quietly where you won't be disturbed. Take a drink to ground yourself when you return. Light a candle or some incense if appropriate. Adjust your clothes and get comfortable.......

Close your eyes and begin to relax.............

When you are ready to begin concentrate on your breathing. Take in a deep breath. Breathe in through your nose. Take the breath deep into your body. Breathe out through your mouth. Breathe in through your nose and out through your mouth, once more in through the nose and out through the mouth. Now still concentrating on your breathing begin to breath naturally.........

You are sitting in a beautiful orchard, the branches of the apple trees are heavy with fruit. Green, red and yellow apples of every shape and size......... Take in a deep breath and smell the lovely appley, cidery aroma.......... On the ground are some fallen apples, blackbirds and robins are enjoying the bounty........... A wasp, drunken with the fermented juice buzzes idly past............

The sky is a gentle blue and the sun makes shapes and patterns on the ground as it peeps through the branches of the trees..........

After a time you get to your feet and walk to the top of the orchard towards a stream that runs down into the orchard from the woodland beyond.......... Go through the gate and into the wood.......... There is a slight incline up through the wood. As you gently climb you notice the oak and holly trees that abound in the area.......... The oak's leaves are now bronzed and beginning to fall to the ground, as you look down the ground is covered with acorns….. You pass the holly, it's glossy leaves shine in the sunlight and there is the promise of an abundant crop of berries………….

At the top of the wood is a quiet country lane. Turn to your right and follow the lane which is lined with oak trees and the occasional holly…….. You hear a noise in the branches, two squirrels appear, chasing one another through the branches and round and round the tree trunks closer to the ground. Suddenly they notice you and scamper away………….

Take a grassy track on your left and begin to walk up the gentle slope….. After a while there is a five bar gate on your left……. Pause and lean on the gate and look at the fantastic view. Fields and trees, sheep and cattle. In the distance you see the top of Dartmoor, it's rocky Tors sparkle and glisten in the afternoon sunlight……………..

Now continue your journey along the path………. You walk through a deserted farmyard. The old barns and stables are now full of wood and mowers instead of animals……….. After you cross the farmyard you see a hedge in front of you……….. Walk towards the gate in the hedge……. As you near the gate you see masses of cyclamen growing wild under the hedge and dry stone walls. Stop to admire their delicate flowers and leaves…………………..

Go through the gate and into more woodland……….. Again it is mostly oak and holly trees with some bracken growing underneath….. You are now beginning to walk downhill and after a while the trees on your right give way to reveal open moorland that is covered in russet coloured bracken………….. In the distance you can see some of the granite Tors…….. There is a bench. Stop and sit on the bench to enjoy the view…………..

When you are ready continue walking downhill to the

valley floor below where you can hear the rush of water......
At last you reach the river in the valley. Again stop and enjoy the time by the river.......... Notice the white swirls and foam as the water flows over stones..... A dipper flies past foraging for his supper........... Turn to look at the ancient humpback bridge that spans the river just here, the huge stones at the base are covered in mosses and lichen.............

When you are ready to leave this space turn to your left and begin to walk along the valley floor following the river......... Once again the oak trees are all around you..... Suddenly walking very slowly towards you is Dartmoor pony, they graze this area to help clear scrub. The pony is grey but by a trick of the light he almost has a purple haze all around him, it makes him seem almost mystical. As you approach one another the pony stops and gently snuffles your shoulder. Tentatively you stroke his soft velvety muzzle. You feel his gentle breath on your hands and in your face.........

After a while the pony begins to move away and you continue your walk along the river bank until you reach the gate at the end of the field........... Go through the gate and back through the orchard and sit once again amongst the apple trees...............

When you feel ready count down from five and come back to the room....... Move your shoulders and head from side to side as you come back to the room. If you lit a candle when you blow it out send love and healing to those in need and take a moment to reflect upon the season. Take some small sips of water to ground yourself.

MISTY AUTUMN MORNING WALK

A mysterious and magical early morning walk. A celebration of Autumn in her full glory. The leaves on the trees vary from green to yellow. From brown to golden russet.

Horse chestnuts, sweet chestnuts, hazel nuts and acorns abound. They fall to the ground all around. Grey Squirrels scurry. Ever busy. A small brown dog tries so hard to catch them, failing each time.

Spider webs shine silver as they are covered with misty dew. Water droplets shimmer and shine. Bright red rosehips shine like bright jewels amongst the burnished gold of the autumn bracken.

Blackberry bushes now mostly bare of fruit their leaves turning to brilliant red and gold before falling silently to the ground.

Birds fly past, mostly silent now emerging and disappearing once again into the misty morning air. Decaying trees fallen in gales past or from the Woodsman's axe are covered in lichen, moss, ferns and fungi.

Upon the ground amongst the dying bracken and fallen leaves puff balls and fly agaric peep between fronds. Beautiful to gaze upon but I shall never pick!

I gaze up between the branching canopy. The sky is beginning to clear. The soft ethereal mist is slowly moving away. The sky is turning from milky white to glorious blue.

Shafts of sunlight pierce the woodlands all around me.
As I emerge from the magical woods to the grassy hillside the
Earth is bathed in sunlight.

I was inspired to write this a few years ago when we were walking from Marldon to Cockington

Samhain

A VILLAGE TALE

*A*s *the Lord of the Harvest three times I come during the Wheel's turn. At Lughnasadh I am cut down, my blood to be spilled for the Land to be reborn. At Mabon, I wear the Horned Crown at the Apple Harvest feast. At Samahin, I am the Lord of the Wild Hunt, the Souls of those who have passed to lead safely across the final bridge to the Summerlands beyond.*

It had been a bumper harvest of both the wheat and barley harvest at Lughnasadh and the fruits and vegetable second harvest at Mabon. The barns were full of wheat to mill for flour and the barley for the village micro brewery was safely stored for the harsh months ahead.

In the houses and cottages, freezers and larders and store cupboards were full. Even now, almost at Samhain, pickles were being made to be stored with the jams made earlier in the year. Cider apples were being picked from the orchard and cheeses of apples were pressed.

Much preparation was made by everyone who lived in the Village for even in the age of modern technology nothing could be done to control the weather. Due to it's remote location the Village was often cut off for days, or in some cases, weeks during the winter months by heavy snowfalls and flooded roads when the snow melted. Everyone looked out for all of their neighbours especially those who were elderly and vulnerable.

Soon it would be time for the third and final harvest. That of the souls of the departed. For Demi and Fin this year was especially poignant. Fin's parents Sweetbriar and Beech had both departed from the mortal world together at the Summer Solstice. A funeral had been held a few days afterwards and they had been buried back in the Village where they had lived for so many years. All who lived in the Village had lined the narrow streets as a mark of respect when Sweetbriar and Beech had been carried to the burial site. Flowers and ivy wreaths had been placed lovingly upon the grave after the ceremony and all had been invited to the orchard for a wake of bread, cheese and cider.

Now preparations were being made for the Wildhunt on Samhain Eve. Those families who had lost a dear one were preparing to take part in the ritual, the other families in the village would all attend to offer support to the bereaved families. The ritual itself would take place amongst the boulders in the orchard.

Homes around the village were dressed with carved pumpkins and ribbons and garlands of ivy. A bonfire was prepared at the edge of the village well away from any trees and property. Demi helped with bread and cake baking for the feast after the ritual, when the souls of the departed had been lead safely across the bridge to the Summerlands beyond.

As ever Fin was very quiet at this time. He spent much of his days wandering alone on the high moors above the Village as he prepared for the most difficult rite of the year.

Samhain dawned grey and overcast, fitting weather for the day ahead. Final preparations were made to the bonfire and to check that no creatures had decided to shelter inside. The feast which was usually laid out on tables outdoors was laid in the village hall instead. The Crows and Ravens that had been assembling all day began to roost in the trees. It would be time soon enough for them to help escort the souls of those departed away from the Village for the very last time.

At dusk everyone who lived in the Village began to congregate in the orchard making a circle. From babes in arms to the older generation, some breathing a sigh of relief that they were not amongst the ones to be lead across the Bridge this year. All were there.

In the circle had been placed photographs of those who had departed since last Samhain alongside any other small mementoes. These would be retrieved after the ritual and taken to the hall to be put in pride of place during the feast so that they would have their place at the table.

A sudden quiet fell upon the crowd as Fin and Demi walked into the centre of the circle. Fin raised his arms in the air and began. "Welcome all to this our most sacred and important rite of the year. Today we say a final farewell to those dear ones we have lost since last Samhain. Those who we have loved for the time they have spent upon this Earth. Some who will have passed at a ripe old age, others will have passed prematurely. All are remembered and our love goes to those who have been left behind. One day all will be reunited, as they in turn, will pass over the Bridge to the Summerlands beyond. Tomorrow the Wheel begins to turn once more as the New Year begins."

The Ritual began with slow pulsing drumming that eventually rose to a crescendo, this was the cue for those present to begin chanting.

"Lady spin your circle, upon this Samhain Eve. The Lord of the Wildhunt is here, his final task to complete. By Raven's wing and Crow's flight, the souls of those departed, to the Summerlands are lead.

When the chanting was over Demi began the Ritual by lighting the candles to welcome the Guardians of the five elements, her black and silver cloak shimmering in the light of the various torches and lanterns the villagers had bought. Demi began by lighting the candle in the Eastern Quarter.

"Spirit and Guardian of the East, of the Air that is all around us, that all need to live. Hail and Welcome." Demi then moved to the southern part of the circle. "Spirit and Guardian of the South, of the Sun and of Fire. All need the fire and light of the Sun to survive, all need the warmth of the fireside during the cold winter months. Hail and Welcome." Demi then moved to the Western Quarter. "Spirit and Guardian of the West. Of Water, all who live upon the Earth need pure cleansing water to survive, to drink, to wash, to live upon or in. Without water this planet would be lifeless and barren. Hail and Welcome." Demi then moved to the Northern Quarter "Spirit and Guardian of the North of the Earth, of the very land we live upon. The land upon which we grow the crops to sustain us. Hail and Welcome." Lastly Demi walked to the centre of the circle to light the final candle. "Spirit and Guardian of Spirit of this Place we welcome you. This special place is our home and we honour you. Hail and Welcome."

After each of the Guardians had been called all present had echoed. *"Hail and Welcome."*

Fin now walked to the centre of the circle. "Our sacred circle has now been cast. The time has now come to say our final farewells to those whom we held dear. I ask one from each family to join us inside the circle." Several stepped forward from the crowd and made their way to the centre of the circle to stand beside the photographs of those who had passed. Each family member bent to pick up the cord that had been tied to the photograph of their family member.

"As we bid our final goodbyes do not be sad for those who have passed from us. All have both happy and sad memories of our family and friends. All are bereft at this parting. All will be reunited one day, as in turn we shall all pass over the bridge where our loved ones will be waiting for us. Now is the time to cut that final cord that binds our loved one to this Earthly plane." Fin then walked from photograph to photograph, at each one he paused then as the family member held the binding cord taut he used his Atheme to sever the cords. Lastly Fin stopped next to the photograph of Sweetbriar and Beech, he picked up the cord and with love and care severed his last ties with his parents.

Fin turned to the crowd. "All is done. Earthly ties are severed. Our departed are free to leave us. Free to cross the Bridge." The crowd echoed Fin.

"All is done. Earthly ties are severed. Our departed are free to leave us. Free to cross the Bridge."

Fin raised his arms for silence. As Demi began to extinguish the candles Fin spoke. "Guardians of the North of the Earth, we give thanks for your presence at our Ritual today. Hail and Farewell. Guardian of the West, of clear pure Waters we give thanks for your presence here today. Hail and Farewell. Guardian of the Fire we give thanks for your presence here today. Hail and Farewell. Guardian of the Air we give thanks for your presence here today. Hail and Farewell. Guardian of The Spirit of this Place we give thanks for your presence here today. *Hail and Farewell."*

After each Guardian had been thanked and dismissed all present echoed. *"Hail and Farewell"*

Fin clapped his hands together. "Our Rite is now over. I shall lead the spirits of those departed to the Bridge at the edge of the village."

Fin walked to the edge of the circle, as he did so, the crowd parted. Fin began the climb up the hill to the top of the Village. The route was lined with carved pumpkins, their small lights shining illuminating his path. Fin had walked this way so many times he didn't really need the lights but they were comforting for the more superstitious in the village. The Crows and Ravens followed behind on silent wings.

As Fin was enveloped by the darkness on the hill the villagers made their way to the hall for the feasting. The bonfire would be lit later and there would be music, dancing and apple bobbing.

At last Fin reached the very top of the hill, the boundary of the Village, were he could pass no further after dark. Fin stopped and turned around. "Go now my friends and family, go to the Summerlands. The way is paved and clear for you to follow." Fin bowed his head in respect as the souls of the departed followed the Crows and Ravens to leave the Village for the very last time. After the last souls had passed he watched Sweetbriar and Beech, their youthful looks and vigor restored, walking hand in hand towards the shining light that was the gateway to the Summerlands. Just before the gateway they stopped and turned and smiled at their only son, each raised a hand in a farewell salute. Fin heard in his head "Until we meet again, Blessed Son."

POEM FOR WITCHES.
PAST AND PRESENT

Sisters and Brothers of times past, we who are now free to practice our Pagan Paths without fear of persecution salute you. Long persecuted for your Strange beliefs. Wise Women and Cunning Men. Often you were turned to in secret for your potions, salves, chants and spells.

Love spells for the love lorn. Potions and salves for both ladies and men's Embarrassing problems and Troubles. Those young girls abused by the Lord of the Manor who were then cast aside when unwanted seeds had been sown.

Those two faced Betters did then to the ducking stool lead you. If you sank or swam the outlook for both was death. Stories of flying broomsticks, familiars and pointed hats. Dancing in woodlands clad in nothing but sky. Your persecutors were many in Salem and Pendle.

Sisters and Brothers, we who are free, whether we be Pagan, Wiccan, Druid or Witch are both angered and humbled by the memories from the long and recent past.
May you now be resting in comfort in the Summerlands.

I was inspired to write this after a visit to the Museum of Witchcraft and Magic in Boscastle and by the memorial to the Pendle Witches in Lancaster park

TINTAGEL

Tintagel you sit and dream amongst the snowy mists. What tales could you tell if only you were able?

Does Merlin lie dreaming beneath your great rocky countenance, one day to return in time of need with the Once and Future King as told in the tales of Arthur, his Knights and a table round.

Tales of peace and battles, of feast and famine. Of great kings and knights and serfs and slaves.
The constant waves crash around your rocky shores.

Sea of deep blue and crests of waves foaming white eroding your solid splendour. Great rocks and caves etched by time and wave.

Gulls screech from above and as we climb ever higher below, diving for fish and scavenging picnic pasties and pies from the unwary.

Wild herbs and flowers sit like jewels amidst your grassy slopes. Were their ancestors used to make salves and potions by Merlin's hand?

As we leave your magical isle we to look again to wonder in awe at your mystical cliffs, turrets and walls.

SAMHAIN MEDITATION

Sit quietly where you won't be disturbed. Take a drink to ground yourself when you return. Light a candle or some incense if appropriate. Adjust your clothes and get comfortable.......

Close your eyes and begin to relax.............

When you are ready to begin concentrate on your breathing. Take in a deep breath. Breathe in through your nose. Take the breath deep into your body. Breathe out through your mouth. Breathe in through your nose and out through your mouth, once more in through the nose and out through the mouth. Now still concentrating on your breathing begin to breath naturally.........

It is mid afternoon..... It is late Autumn..... It is Samhain Eve..... You are looking over a picket gate into a walled garden............. The vegetable beds are now almost bare. There are some leeks and swedes in a bed a little way off and closest to you is the herb garden.....There is still plenty of sage and rosemary the more tender herbs have now died or been removed to a greenhouse..... Open the gate and bend to rub the leaves of the sage, it's pungent aroma fills the air. Take in a deep breath savouring the perfume................ Now pick some of the rosemary............. Bruise the leaves and again savour the aroma................ Now, taking the rosemary branches with you, turn and leave the garden...............

You cross a lawn and head for the path that skirts the edge of the garden............ It has open views to your left. On your right there is a dense woodland. Take the path........... In the distance you glimpse the sea........... On this grey and overcast day it looks dark and foreboding......... As you walk you look down on the open ground to your left……… The once brilliant green ferns that cover this ground are now turning a deep dark russet……….. The gorse that dots the area is, as ever, in bloom, it's brilliant yellow flowers are a welcome sight on this dull day…………..

Look to your right into the wood……… The leaves have almost all fallen, they cover the woodland floor……….. Near you at the edge of the wood is a drystone wall. The wall is covered in small ferns and navel wort, there are still some of the delicate pink flowers in bloom. As you look closer you can see lichens and mosses on the wall and also on the trunks of the trees. As you look upwards you see the moss often referred to as Witches Whiskers covering the branches of several trees…………...

Look forward now down towards the sea and beach in the distance, the waves are gently lapping the shore line and the horizon between sea and sky is blurred…………...

Look down at the edge of the path……… Everywhere there are toadstools and mushrooms. Brown, silver, grey and the bright red Fly Agaric. Stop to admire the fungus….. Notice that some of them are broken off and turned upside down. You can clearly see the gills on the underside of the toadstools and the small insects and flies that call them home. You can smell the musty decay …………...

Begin walking once more, drawing ever closer to the beach…………..Just before the path begins to go downhill onto the beach there is a small grassy area with a wooden shelter that is enclosed on three sides. It is open to the elements the side that faces the beach……….. Stop and sit inside the shelter enjoying the view and the gentle breeze blowing in from the sea………... Place the rosemary on the seat beside you, inviting someone to join you…………...

As you watch the waves gently lapping the sandy beach you

are aware of another presence come to sit beside you. Welcome the visitor............Sit in companionable silence............ Do they have a message for you?............

Your visitor has now gone. It is beginning to get dark, twilight is settling but just as you are about to leave your seat the sun suddenly pops out from behind a cloud as it often does when it is about to set............. It casts brilliant streaks of light upon the sea.............. Now retrace your steps past the woodland and open ground and then back to the garden and home..............

When you are ready slowly begin count down from five. Move your shoulders and head from side to side as you come back to the room. If you lit a candle when you blow it out send love and healing to those in need and take a moment to reflect upon the season. Take some small sips of water to ground yourself.

Yule

A VILLAGE TALE

Yuletide is here, the birth of the Sun God we celebrate.
Holly, Mistletoe and Ivy decorate our homes and hearths.
The Holly and Oak in a woodland clearing do battle.
Tales of magic and mystery pass the long Winter evenings.

Demi and Fin stood in one of their favourite places, at the top of the Village overlooking the valley and the craggy granite moors in the distance. The short winter day was ending and the sun was setting, a fiery dark red globe in a red, orange and blue sky signified a sharp overnight frost with clear sunny skies tomorrow. "Yule blessings." Said Fin as he took Demi in his arms, kissing her passionately. Suddenly Demi broke away. "Oh! I think it's begun." Sudden cramping pains had gripped Demi and she had doubled over, Fin supporting her. "Aaah! Yes. Its time to head for home." Demi and Fin knew that their son would be born before the morning sunrise but had expected to make it home before Demi's labour started. "Good thing we haven't far to go. Seems he is impatient to join us for the Yule celebrations tomorrow." Laughed Fin. "It would seem so." Smiled Demi.

Fin helped Demi home to their cottage at the edge of the village. On the way they passed a small group of villagers who had also been watching the sunset. They realised at once that Demi was in labour. "Shall we fetch the midwife and Sarah and Mike?" "Please. I don't want to leave Demi alone."

Quickly the group made their way to the heart of the village to alert Sarah and Mike, Demi's parents and Diana the midwife who lived locally.

When they reached their cottage Fin made some raspberry leaf tea for Demi, she had been drinking it through the latter stages of her pregnancy and Fin felt that he needed something to do to keep his mind occupied.

In a very short time Diana arrived, closely followed by Sarah and Mike. Demi was spending her time trying to regulate her breathing and walking around the small sitting room. "How are you doing?" Asked Diana when she arrived. "Let's take you upstairs so I can check you over and we can prepare the room for birthing. Sarah can help, when all is ready Fin may join us."

Demi, Diana and Sarah made their way upstairs to the largest of the two bedrooms.

"Mum if you look in the wardrobe you will see the birthing pack all ready and all of the clothes for the baby are in his room." Sarah busied herself finding the pack and then she and Diana made up the bed ready for Demi. "All coming along nicely, just as expected." Said Diana smiling. You can either stay here now or go back downstairs with Fin and Mike. Demi looked at the rather steep staircase, she had run up and down them several times a day over the years, but she was unsure if she would be able to make them in the latter stages of labour. Courage overtook her. "Yes, OK lets all go back downstairs for a while. I am sure a cup of tea is in order for everyone."

With Diana leading the way they all went back to the sitting room. Fin looked more than a little worried. "Are you sure this is OK for you to be down here?" He asked anxiously. "Yes I am fine, I don't need to be upstairs until things get going a little more." Smiled Demi.

By now word had got around the village that the birth of the new Lord of the Wildwood was imminent. It had not escaped the notice of some of the more observant older ladies of the village that there were a lot of comings and goings centred around Demi and Fin's cottage. Of course they all knew that by sunrise the following day the child would be born. In the closest cottage to Demi and Fin's one of these Observant Ladies lived. It was to her cottage that several other Observant Ladies made their way for tea and cakes and speculation as for the exact timing of the birth. Sleep was now impossible as their excitement grew.

"I bet it's three o'clock." Said one. "Don't be silly it will be closer to four." Said another. "Now, now, it will be at sunrise of course." Observed another. "The babe will come when he's good and ready and not before. All this speculation is getting us nowhere." Intoned the owner of the cottage. "More tea and cake anyone?" At this all of the Observant Ladies temporarily forgot everything in favour of refilling plates and mugs. Something stronger would wait until the actual announcement.

Outside the moon shone brightly from a clear star studded sky. She was waxing to fullness in a few days time. There were no street lights in the Village, the moon and stars lit up the streets and village green, torches were not needed to see the way. An Owl hooted in the nearby woodlands and a fox crept through the orchard in search of his supper. The badgers were sleeping deep underground and the bats were roosting in attic spaces throughout the village.

Most families slept on as they knew that they would be up early the following morning as excited children would want to see what small hand crafted gifts they had received for Yule. This year they knew that this was to be an extra special Yule as the new Son of the Lady of the Land and Harvest and the Lord of the Wildwood would be born. Yule feasts had been prepared ready the previous day, for all to share in the village hall, after the greeting of the Sunrise and the traditional battle between the Oak and Holly Kings. This year it would be a special feast to greet the birth of the new child.

In Demi and Fin's cottage time was passing. Demi's pains suddenly began to come much closer together and she gripped Fin's hand much tighter. "I think I need to go upstairs now." Said Demi. Diana had just examined Demi. "Yes things are going well." Began Diana as Demi suddenly felt that she needed to push. Quickly Mike left the room to grab the birthing kit from upstairs leaving Sarah, Fin and Demi downstairs with Diana. Mike arrived with the pack and put the sheets ready on the floor. Suddenly it seemed as though it was all over. Before Demi could even begin to pant she gave one push and their son was born. "Impatient little fella aren't you?" Said Fin as Diana placed the child upon Demi's chest. There followed tears and hugs of joy as everyone gave thanks for the safe delivery of Demi and Fin's new Son.

In the nearby cottage where the Observant Ladies had gathered one of the ladies also had very sharp hearing. "Shhh!!" She commanded. A sudden hush fell over the room. "He's here, he's arrived. I hear crying." Sure enough now all the ladies could hear the child crying lustily. "Now, well, I said close to four o'clock." Said one of the ladies, "And it is too." They all looked at the clock. "Aye you be right." They all chorused. "Never mind about that." Said the owner of the cottage. "Who is for something to wet the baby's head?" Glasses and mulled cider were produced and yet more cake. They raised their glasses for what would be the first of many toasts that day. "Blessings to the new child and his parents. May he grow strong and protect and guard our Village for many a year."

In Demi and Fin's cottage it was decided nothing could beat a quiet cup of tea and some buttered toast. Everyone was far too tired to think of mulled cider, that would come later. After a final check over for Demi and her child Diana left the cottage and made her way home. By now the news of the safe arrival of Demi and Fin's Son had travelled all around the village and some stopped to chat to Diana in an attempt to find out news. "What does he weigh?" "Who does he look like?" What is his name?" To all of these questions Diana replied with a smile. "You will all hear soon enough. Fin will announce it later when he and Demi have decided."

After a hearty breakfast the villagers began to assemble in the orchard near the large stone for the Yule or Midwinter Sunrise ceremony. The sky was clear with the promise of a spectacular sunrise. This year Fin would be leading the ceremony alone as Demi would not be able to join him. As Fin approached the stone many clapped him on the shoulder or whispered, "Congratulations." Fin felt as though he could burst with pride. He had found it difficult to leave Demi even though Sarah and Mike were staying with her.

When Fin reached the stone he climbed to the top and raised his hands in acknowledgement of the huge cheer that erupted. "Thank you all so much for your good wishes and congratulations. Later today we shall introduce our new son to you all." "What's his name?" Someone shouted. "Later." Laughed Fin. "All the details later. Now we need to greet the Solstice sunrise. The Sunrise waits for no one." At this everyone began to face towards the horizon to await the sunrise. The sky was shot with blue, orange and gold and then a little after eight o'clock the sun climbed over the horizon and filled the orchard with piercing light. Everyone began to drum and chant;

Yuletide is here, the birth of the Sun God we celebrate.
Holly, Mistletoe and Ivy decorate our homes and hearths.
The Holly and Oak in a woodland clearing do battle.
Tales of magic and mystery pass the long Winter evenings.
After the chanting and drumming. Fin raised his hands and everyone became silent. "We have greeted our Solstice Dawn.

We have greeted the rebirth of the Sun and the return of the light to the Land. Now welcome our new Son!" To everyone's delight Mike strode to the rock and passed the child to Fin. Fin held up the child for all to see. "Welcome to our new Son. One day he will become the new Lord of the Wildwood. Welcome Oak into your lives and hearts." As Fin spoke he held up the child for all to see. The Sun rising in the sky framed Fin and Oak bathing them in an orange and red glow. The crowd erupted into a chorus of "Well done. Congratulations." Much clapping and cheering and drumming rang out. Oak lay peacefully in Fin's arms sleeping through all of the fuss. After a while Fin handed Oak back to Mike. The crowd parted as Mike passed taking Oak back to the warmth and comfort of Demi's arms.

"Now." Said Fin. "It is the time for the Oak and Holly Kings to do battle." Everyone headed for the large clearing towards the top of the orchard. The nominated Oak and Holly kings stepped forward each dressed in their pale or dark green costumes with either a crown of oak or holly leaves. Fin stepped into the centre of the clearing. "Oak King. Are you ready for battle to reclaim your rightful crown?" "I am!" Cried the Oak King. "Holly King are you ready to relinquish your crown to the new rightful king?" "I am, but not without a proper challenge." Replied the Holly King. "Then let the battle commence." Ordered Fin.

The Oak King and the Holly King stepped forward into the centre of the clearing. Sounds of steel clashing onto steel filled the air. Backwards and forwards they battled until at last the Holly King gave way. He removed his crown of holly leaves and kneeling in front of the Oak King he relinquished his thorny crown. Fin walked to the centre of the clearing and standing in front of the fallen Holly King raised him to his feet. All present then bowed to the Oak King;

"All praise to our new Oak King. May he rule and guide us

forward towards the light and the Summer Solstice. Blessed Be."

After much cheering and drumming Fin raised his hands into the air for silence. "Now it is time for our Winter Solstice feast. Let us make our way to the hall for the feast and to raise our glasses to the new Oak King and to the new Lord of the Wildwood who was born this day.

Everyone gathered in the hall, glasses had already been filled with either mulled cider or mulled apple juice so that everyone could collect a glass as they filed into the hall. When all was ready Fin asked for a drum roll. "To our new Oak King. May he grow in stature and stand tall and proud until the Midsummer when he will once again begin to lose his powers." "The Oak King!" When all had raised the toast Fin once again raised his glass. "Now it is time to raise your glasses in greeting to our Son, Oak." Whilst all present were raising their glasses to toast their son, Demi, Sarah and Mike entered the hall and joined Fin at the table. Demi took her seat and Sarah and Mike in their turn joined in the toast to their new Grandson. "To Oak. The new Lord of the Wildwood." "Oak!" Echoed everyone. "Now let the feasting begin!" Cried Fin.

Demi and Oak remained at the hall for the Yule feast. Oak slept through all of the noise blissfully unaware of everything going on in his honour. After the feast many of the villagers came to offer their individual congratulations and to admire the new baby. When the singing and dancing started Demi and Fin and Sarah and Mike decided it was time to head for home and an early night. As they walked towards their cottage the almost full moon shone from a starry sky in it's turn pouring blessings upon the new arrival. Demi and Fin exchanged a brief kiss as they cuddled their new son.

As for the Observant Ladies, after all of the previous night's excitement, they were fast asleep at their tables in the hall.

YULE

Flickering candlelight reflects on horns brimming with mead.

Spicy cinnamon sticks, ribbons and pine cones hang from our trees of evergreen.

The fragrance of pine resin fills the air.

We decorate our homes with mistletoe and holly, red berries shining bright

As we walk through the frosty night dragon's breath hangs in the air.

Long winter walks over frozen fields, frost nips at our fingers and toes.

Glimpses of deer and fox as we pass by.

Birds huddle around our garden feeders, we break the ice on the pond.

Home to warm fireside, spiced cake and mulled wine.

YULE MEDITATION

Sit quietly where you won't be disturbed. Take a drink to ground yourself when you return. Light a candle or some incense if appropriate. Adjust your clothes and get comfortable.......

Close your eyes and begin to relax.............

When you are ready to begin concentrate on your breathing. Take in a deep breath. Breathe in through your nose. Take the breath deep into your body. Breathe out through your mouth. Breathe in through your nose and out through your mouth, once more in through the nose and out through the mouth. Now still concentrating on your breathing begin to breath naturally.........

It is Mid- Winter and you are standing in a snowy garden. The bench where you sit on long lazy summer days is now covered in snow, you can see small footprints in the snow where garden birds have hopped over the surface............. Turn to your left, the garden pond and fountain is silent. The water is now an icy film and from the fountain long fragile icicles hang, they sparkle and glimmer in the winter sunlight.............. Turn to your right and head for the garden gate, the climbing roses that are burst of colour and fragrance in midsummer are now sprinkled with snow and all around the world is silent............. Open the garden gate and pass under the rose arch into the field beyond........... In summer this field is a mass of wild flowers, it is now fallow. The seeds from last Autumn lie under the covering of snow. They await the time when the Earth begins to rewarm and they may germinate once more to become a riot of colour and feeding insects, bees and butterflies. Walk along the hedge line at the edge of the field towards the wood in the distance..................

You reach the silent woods. The trees are bare of all leaves except the King of the Woods, the Holly, his glossy leaves and berries shine in the Winter sun........... Pause a while to admire this ever enduring tree so revered by everyone for its berries and splash of colour at this dark time of the year.......... You see a small movement and as you look a Robin sits quietly on a branch in the heart of the tree sheltering from the cold, its bright eyes watch you as you stand in silence................ After a time turn away and begin to walk through the woods. As you walk you notice the structure of the trees and of the branches. The branches seem like arms that reach up towards the sky. You notice the thick green mosses at the base of the trees............ Stop and reach out your hands to touch the nearest tree. The moss feels smooth and even in the snowy landscape warm to the touch. You wonder how many small insects and mammals are sheltering inside. You feel at one with the tree and with the landscape and nature all around...............

Continue up through the woods. Now concentrate on the snowy ground........... Everywhere is a mass of footprints. Birds of all kinds. Robin, sparrow, blackbird, crow, fox, badger and deer. You notice one particular set deer of prints and begin to follow them........... The short Winter day is beginning to draw to a close as you follow the footprints............You decide to follow them for just a few more minutes before turning for home............... The prints lead you up a small incline towards the top of the woodland. It is now beginning to feel very cold. Just as you think you will turn for home you stop in amazement............... In front of you at the top of the incline a magnificent Stag is standing in a snowy clearing. The setting Sun seems held in the tines of his antlers. The Stag stands tall and proud, his neck arched. You stop transfixed by this wonderful sight...............

After a while the Stag tosses his head and turns and walks slowly away........... You too turn and begin the walk back the way you have come. Through the woods............ Back along the hedgerow............. Through the garden gate back to the garden and then home to the warmth of the fireside..............

When you are ready, slowly begin count down from five. Move your shoulders and head from side to side as you come back to the room. If you lit a candle when you blow it out send love and healing to those in need and take a moment to reflect upon the season. Take some small sips of water to ground yourself.

THE FIVE QUARTERS

I look to the East, Spirit of the Air.
A new dawn.
A new day.
A new beginning, a new life.

I look to the South, Spirit of fire.
For warmth.
For the sunrise.
And sunset.

I look to the West, Spirit of Water.
Upon which all life on earth depends.
Life giving springs, small streams becoming mighty rivers.
That flow to the sea.

I look to the North, Spirit of Earth.
From which we all come.
To which we must all return.
I see night and endings.

I thank the Spirit of Place, wherever I may be.
It's beauty, peace and calmness, tranquil harmony.
I see nature all around.
All the elements surround me.

Part Two

STORIES FOR A COLD WINTER EVENING

A YULETIDE STORY

Sally started and opened her eyes. The full moon shining through the window had woken her from a deep slumber. Quickly she sat up in bed and looked at the clock, it was six thirty, she was due to meet her friend Cerys at a Christmas Eve party at eight o'clock. Sally ran for the shower.

When Sally was ready she grabbed the bottle of red wine she had bought to take with her and rushed out of the door. The night was very cold and a mist was beginning to rise as she made her way to her car.

Once inside the car Sally checked the address for the party and the Sat Nav settings. "Hmm, Old Stone Manor, sounds very grand, though quite a drive and fairly remote. Mr David Lupon. I don't even know the guy. He is supposed to be a friend of Cerys. I only agreed to go because she didn't want to go on her own." Sally muttered to herself as she started the car.

After a while Sally turned off the main roads and began to drive some rather deserted country lanes, all very new territory. Sally was used to bright lights and wine bars, not grand sounding country piles up roads that were little more than farm tracks in some places.

"You have reached your destination." The Sat Nav's insistent voice broke into Sally's reverie as she turned into a very imposing looking driveway. In the distance through the now fairly thick fog Sally could just make out some very dimly lit windows. "It's not very festive looking." She grumbled. Perhaps I can persuade Cerys to leave early so we can get back to town and Vance's wine bar before they close thought Sally as she parked her car outside the deserted Manor house.

Sally sat in the car for several minutes hoping that Cerys would soon arrive or at least another guest so she would have some company when she went into the party.

Eventually, very reluctantly, Sally left the warmth of her car and headed up the impressive flight of steps that lead to the front door. Sally stood outside the door for a few moments looking in vain for signs of any cars arriving, or at least some headlights in the distance.

By now Sally was feeling very cold, vulnerable and lonely. Should she brave the party alone or just head back home. The fog if anything was becoming thicker. Sally checked her phone. No signal. Perhaps the party had been cancelled as the weather had deteriorated and as Sally had no phone signal Cerys had not been able to contact her. Sally decided to ring the door bell to ask if the party had been cancelled or if Cerys had left her any message.

Gingerly Sally tugged at the bell rope, she heard the distant ringing of the bell somewhere deep inside the gloomy house.

When Sally was just about to give up and go home anyway, or at least to drive to where she had a phone signal, she heard footsteps approaching the door. The door was opened by the sort of Butler you only read about in an Agatha Christie novel. "Yerrs?" Said the Butler. Sally stammered "Oh, oh. I am here for the party. I am meeting my friend Cerys here. The fog is so bad perhaps she can't find the house. Has the party been cancelled?" The words tumbled out, Sally was now so nervous she wished she had never left home.

"The party is still going ahead." Replied the Butler. "Where are the other guests, I don't see any other cars." Sally said miserably. "The other guests are around and they have all parked at the back of the house." This was said in such a tone that Sally felt even more inferior and more than a little stupid, she realised that the front of the house was probably far too grand to allow just anyone to park there.

Pensively Sally stepped across the threshold, she heard the door close quietly behind her. A shiver ran up her spine. "This way." Said the Butler. "Your host is expecting you." Sally followed the Butler across the vast entrance hall, the walls and staircase she noticed were covered in portraits. "Probably all by Rembrandt or Gainsborough." Thought Sally. Sally had little knowledge of famous painters these were just names she knew. Sally also noticed that there had been no effort to decorate the house in any way to reflect the festive season.

The Butler opened some double doors and then stood to one side so that Sally could enter the room. Standing next to a massive fireplace with his back to the room stood a man in evening dress. As the Butler closed the door behind Sally the man slowly turned to face her. Sally was somewhat taken aback as the man was about her own age, mid twenties, with black wavy hair and the most enormous brown eyes that Sally had ever seen.

"I'm Sally, I have come for the party….." Sally began. "But, but where is everyone? Your Butler said that everyone else had parked to the rear of your house."

The man walked towards Sally the firelight reflecting in his eyes. He extended his arm in order to shake Sally's hand. "My name is David your host for the evening. Sally. Such a tasteful name. Come let us have a drink."

"Where is everyone else?" Sally asked again. A feeling of strange attraction but also dread overcame her. "They are about somewhere, this is a large house and people just drift from room to room, or hang around." David replied.

David lead Sally to a sofa, as they sat down he handed Sally a large glass of brandy. "To keep out the winter chills."

Sally held the glass in her hands, she raised the glass to her lips and had a sip. The spirit burned as it ran down her throat. Sally shuddered, white wine or Prosecco were her usual choices.

"So have you lived in this house a long time?" Asked Sally trying desperately to make conversation. "Oh forever." Replied her host. "Err should we go and join the other guests, I don't want to monopolise all of your attention."

"We can join them later, it will shortly be supper time." Was it Sally's imagination or was there a reddish glint in David's brown eyes? "Let me show you around the Manor House." David stood up and Sally followed his lead. They crossed the room to a door on the further corner from where Sally had entered. David opened the door and stood to one side to allow Sally to exit the room in front of him. The room opened up to a long gallery which was full of suits of armour, swords and objects of torture. Sally stopped as if glued to the spot her eyes filled with horror at the spectacle in front of her. "Do you not like my little museum?" Asked David. "This is all now very harmless and just here as a piece of fun, a talking point for all of my many guests."

"Talking of your fellow guests when will I get to meet them?" Asked Sally yet again. By now she was feeling increasingly uneasy and was attempting to find the right phrasing to make her excuses to leave. "I was supposed to be meeting my friend Cerys here, do you happen to know if she has already arrived and may be waiting for me in another room. She will be getting anxious by now." "All in good time." Said David. "Cerys arrived a while ago and she has been looked after already." Again that reddish glow in David's eyes. Sally looked down was it her imagination playing yet more tricks or were David's finger nails longer than when he had shaken her hand earlier.

Sally decided it was high time she did some thinking. "It was a long journey here, umm could I use your bathroom before we meet the other guests and we have some supper?"

"But of course, it is this way." David pointed to a door at the end of the long gallery. Sally hastened towards it and upon reaching the door wrenched it open, shot inside and quickly locked the door, trying to steady her shaking hands.

Once alone Sally almost felt as though she was imagining all of her fears, as soon as she left the smallest room she would ask to join Cerys and then just make her excuses to both Cerys and David and leave. She could plead the bad weather or the fact that she had to be up very early the following day. She had volunteered to help out at the local homeless shelter to serve Christmas Day lunches. Yes, yes Sally decided that would be the best plan.

Sally took several deep breaths. "Right Sally be calm, stay calm. Breathe." She said to herself. Just as she was about to unlock the door Sally heard a strange snuffling and scraping outside of the door. Sally froze. Once again her fears surfaced. Thoughts of haunted houses crossed her mind. "Oh for goodness sake girl get a grip. It's only a draught these country piles are notoriously difficult to keep warm." Sally took the bull by the horns, or in this case the door lock and handle and opened the door. David was standing several paces away. "Ah there you are. Comfortable now?" He asked smiling. "Yes thank you."

Nothing ventured nothing gained thought Sally. "Please could you take me to the room where Cerys and the other guests are now." Asked Sally. "I have a very early start tomorrow helping out at the homeless shelter, I am afraid I won't be able to stay for supper after all. I just need to explain to Cerys before I leave."

"Very well follow me." David turned and lead the way to yet another door, this time when he opened the door the room was in darkness. "I will just put the light on for you." Began David as he shoved Sally through the door. The light came on to reveal a kitchen, the centre piece of which was a butcher's block. Sitting in the centre of the block in a pool of congealed blood was Cerys' head it's eyes bulging, her once beautiful red hair lying listless all around.

Sally screamed and turned to run. David grabbed her arm, she turned and bit his hand. David let out a howl of pain and let her go. Sally ran as fast as she could to the far end of the gallery away from David, she tugged open the door and rushed across the hallway to the front door. She wrenched open the front door, car keys already in her hand, she sped down the steps towards where she had parked her car. Sally stopped dead in her tracks. Where was her car she knew she had left it just at the base of the steps. Sally heard a voice behind her "Looking for something Miss?" Sally turned, the Butler was standing right behind her. "I took the liberty of moving your vehicle, it made the front of the Manor look so untidy." "But I have the keys." Said Sally. "Before I was in service here with his Lordship I used to hot wire cars to order, your cheap little car was no challenge at all."

Suddenly Sally felt rather than heard someone or something approaching from the rear of the Manor. She turned. The fog suddenly began to disappear and brilliant moonlight shone upon David who had just begun to remove his shirt, his jacket had obviously been discarded some time ago. Sally could see that his thick wavy black hair now covered not only his face but his body too. Sally ran heading across the wide expanse of lawns next to the driveway hoping that if she made it to the road a car may be passing that she could flag down. David now on all fours howled to the moonlight and began to give chase. Sally ran as fast as she could, the muscles in her legs beginning to burn. Suddenly David was upon her and with his red drooling jaws wrapped around one of her arms he began to drag Sally back towards the Manor. The Butler ran across the lawns, he picked Sally up and threw her across his shoulder. "I will take this trouble maker straight to the kitchen Sir."

Sally was powerless to fight back as she lay across the Butler's powerful shoulders. David loped along beside them, licking the blood from Sally's arm wound from around his jowls.

Up the flight of steps, in through the front door and across the hallway. Through the grand sitting room they went, then into the long gallery museum towards the doorway that lead into the kitchen where Sally had seen what had remained of Cerys.

Sally began to scream and scream. "HELP! HELP!" She was too angry for tears, she felt her fate was already sealed and she would shortly end up like Cerys. Suddenly Sally heard a movement from behind one of the suits of armour, she looked up and saw what looked like two of the swords twirling in mid air as someone emerged from the shadows. The Butler stopped short. "Who are you! This is a private party in a private house we are just having a bit of fun, no room for gatecrashers."

The swords didn't falter. "Oh no you don't not this time." Said Sally's saviour. "Drop the girl!" The swords came closer. Suddenly one of the swords lunged towards David cutting a deep slash in his side the other sword came down with a mighty blow on the Butler's legs he shrieked and dropped Sally who rolled away as far as possible. The swords then came down again on David getting him right between the ribs straight into his heart. David lay dead. The Butler had already made his escape unseen by both Sally and Swords.

Swords produced a small pistol, he turned and fired the pistol into David's limp body. "Silver Bullet." Swords explained. "You can't be too careful in cases like these."

"What cases?" Asked Sally. "Lycanthropy." Replied Swords. "Or to put it another way your host was a Werewolf. I have been investigating this place for several months now." Sally suddenly began to feel very light headed and before Swords could catch her she collapsed to the floor……

Sally started and opened her eyes. The full moon shining through the window had woken her from a deep slumber. Quickly she sat up in bed and looked at the clock, it was six thirty she was due to meet her friend Cerys at a Christmas Eve party at eight o'clock. Sally ran for the shower. What a dreadful dream thought Sally. As she did so her eyes fell upon the invitation to the party. Mr David Lupton requests the pleasure of the company of Miss Sally Davies…………..

THE WATCHER

Jerby sighed. He checked the clock on his office wall once again, only four forty five. Another fifteen minutes until he could switch off his laptop for the day and head home. He had spent the whole day clock watching between his laptop, wall clock and mobile phone, he couldn't wait until this evening as tonight was the night of the Big Date.

Jerby had been waiting for this evening for months now, his patience was at long last being rewarded.

It had all started last winter when he had first laid eyes on Harriet. He had been out for the evening at the annual work Christmas Do. This sort of social occasion was not at all Jerby's scene, he was more of a loner, preferring his own company or that of his laptop, television or a good book. However he felt as a junior partner in the accountancy company he must go along to join in the general season of goodwill. As in previous years, the evening had ended with most of the staff, having consumed far too much alcohol, leaving partnered up in various taxis for nights of unbridled lust and debauchery. This was then usually to be followed by much embarrassment the following day and in some cases for several weeks. Of course it had been known that the alcoholic removal of inhibitions had resulted in some couples, who had been far too shy to start a relationship during working hours, had finally been bought together and all had ended happily ever after.

Jerby had been to the bar to put another round of drinks on the firm's tab. As he had struggled through the throng of revellers at the nightclub he had almost tripped and tipped the whole tray of drinks over Harriet. "Oh, I am so sorry I didn't see you there." Said Jerby. Jerby gasped as he realised he was staring at the most beautiful girl he had ever seen. He realised just in time that his mouth was hanging open, he shut it promptly and smiled an awkward smile. Jerby was rather shy around girls and females in general and his romantic endeavours had been pitiful, stumbling affairs to say the least.

Harriet had a mane of raven coloured hair, deep brown eyes, perfect white teeth and a pale complexion which is often referred to as An English Rose. As Jerby stood staring Harriet smiled her beautiful smile, Jerby felt as though he was falling into a deep bottomless pool as he looked into those hypnotic brown eyes.

"Um I. I'm Jeremy but everyone calls me Jerby." Stammered Jerby as usual stuck for words in the company of the opposite sex. It was no accident that Jerby's secretary was in late middle age and what is often referred to rather unkindly as frumpy. "Hi, I'm Harriet." Replied Harriet. "Why don't you get rid of those drinks and come back for a drink and a chat?" Jerby couldn't believe his luck. He, Jerby being asked for a drink by this total vision of loveliness. "Oh err yes, be right back." Stammered Jerby.

The rest of the evening followed in a complete daze. Jerby couldn't believe how he could talk so easily to Harriet all his awkwardness around women seemed to have vanished. At the end of the evening Jerby asked Harriet for her phone number. "Oh tell you what you let me have your number and I will phone you." Said Harriet.

That was six months ago.

Much to Jerby's bitter disappointment he had heard nothing more from Harriet. He consoled himself initially that it had been the Christmas and New Year break. He knew that unlike himself most people had families or friends to spend the holidays with. Jerby had been an only child and both of his parents had died in an accident several years ago. As ever Jerby spent the festive period alone with just his books and the television for company.

January came and went as did February. Jerby knew by then that Harriet was never going to get in touch again. "Why would she?" He asked himself. Harriet was a rare beauty who probably had loads of friends and probably had a boyfriend already, or even a live in partner. She was possibly bored that evening at the nightclub and Jerby was just there to chat to to help the evening pass. In his sorry state Jerby told himself that Harriet had just felt sorry for him and all along she had never meant to contact him. The passionate goodnight kiss that evening long ago had obviously not meant anything to her.

One evening in early March Jerby was waiting for the bus home when out of the corner of his eye he glimpsed a girl very like Harriet over on the other side of the road. Jerby sighed would he ever see Harriet again.

Harriet watched Jerby as he waited for his bus, she hoped he had just had a very brief look at her before the bus arrived. Harriet had been very careful up to now to ensure that Jerby had never seen her as she had followed him most evenings throughout the winter. Now she felt it was time to put her plan into action.

It was no accident that Jerby had bumped into Harriet that night at the club. She had deliberately placed herself behind him so that he could do nothing but bump into her as he turned around with the tray of drinks. She had then had no problems in persuading him to have a drink with her and to spend the evening together. She felt the seed had well and truly been sown for his attraction to her after she had given him such a come on, and the kiss at the end of the evening would have fired his passion.

The next evening when Jerby was waiting for his bus he spotted the girl again. Yes, yes it was indeed Harriet. When the bus arrived he hid behind the shelter and waited for the bus to move off to watch where Harriet went. Harriet walked away in the opposite direction to where Jerby lived. Quickly Jerby set off in pursuit being careful not to let Harriet see him. Harriet was very well aware that Jerby was following her and she was careful not to get too far ahead so that he didn't lose sight of her. Reaching home at last Harriet made a pantomime of checking her roses for greenfly before she went indoors, she glanced very carefully in Jerby's direction before going inside to make sure he had followed her.

After that evening Jerby stopped going home after work. Instead he walked to Harriets home and watched from a safe distance. He stayed until it was time for the last bus home. Once home Jerby crashed into bed totally exhausted. Each evening Harriet checked the street from her bedroom window to ensure Jerby was watching the house.

Jerby began to be a shadow of his former self. He lost weight and had trouble concentrating on his work. His fellow workmates began to comment how pale and ill Jerby looked, so much so that his devoted secretary began to bring him in sandwiches and cakes from home to ensure he had enough to eat. Jerby's boss called him into his office one day and asked if all was well. Jerby assured his boss that he was well but just had one or two things on his mind at the moment.

In late March the phone calls began. One evening when Jerby was watching Harriet's house his mobile rang making him start guiltily. "Hello." Jerby could not believe it when he heard Harriet's voice. "Hi Jerby, it's me Harriet. Sorry not to have called before, I have been away working but I'm back now and I thought I would give you a call."Jerby could not stop himself from looking across at Harriet's house. He knew that Harriet was lying and that she had been doing nothing of the sort. He also knew that she had not been out in the evenings for weeks, at least not when he had been watching the house. The phone calls then came each evening. After a few evenings instead of going to Harriet's house to watch her movements Jerby began to go home again. He began to eat properly and to sleep properly each night. He tried not to think of the reasons Harriet had deliberately lied to him about her whereabouts. She obviously didn't have a boyfriend or live in lover as Jerby had never seen anyone else enter or leave the house. In fact Jerby had never seen Harriet leave the house, he just knew that she was at home because the house had an occupied look about it.

The difference in Jerby was apparent almost immediately.

He began to put on weight and looked much less pale and had more energy. He could concentrate once more on his work. Everyone in his office, not least his secretary breathed a sigh of relief happy to have the old Jerby back.

After a couple of weeks of phone calls Harriet suggested The Date. "How about coming to my place for supper one evening?" Jerby's heart skipped a beat. "When were you thinking?" Jerby tried to keep the excitement out of his voice. "How about the long May Bank holiday weekend. Say you come along for eight o'clock for supper on the Friday evening and we can see how the evening and weekend pans out after that. Jerby couldn't believe his luck. Not only a date. Supper at Harriet's place and by the sounds of it a whole weekend too.

Harriet smiled at the end of the call, that was just delightfully easy, just like reeling in a plump fish. Jerby had also made the classic mistake of not asking Harriet for her address.

Five o'clock at last! Jerby closed his laptop and almost galloped from the building. He just about remembered to wish his secretary and fellow workmates happy long weekend.

Jerby rushed home to shower and change. He thought he should take at least a toothbrush with him as Harriet had hinted the possibility of a long weekend together. Jerby had also paid an all important visit to the machine in the gents loo.

At last Jerby was ready. Essentials and toothbrush in his pockets he set out for Harriets home. Harriet was in her bedroom keeping watch for Jerby, when she saw him approaching she unlocked the front door. Jerby rang the front door bell. "It's open just come straight in." He heard Harriet call. Jerby stepped over the threshold. "In here." Called Harriet. Jerby walked into the lounge. "I thought we could have a drink before food." Said Harriet a smile on her face, again Jerby noticed her deep brown eyes and perfect white teeth. Harriet handed Jerby a glass of red wine. "Cheers." "Cheers." Echoed Jerby.

Over drinks they chatted about this and that. Jerby suddenly realised that over that past few weeks their phone conversations had all been about him and that he knew very little about Harriet. "What do you do for a living, you know job?" Asked Jerby. "Oh this and that. It's mostly night work so I spend most of my days sleeping." "And of course you do spend some time away from home working." Said Jerby, hoping to catch out Harriet's lie. "Oh yes I do have to go away from time to time. Again it's for my living." Replied Harriet, a small smile on her face, yet again showing those perfect teeth.

Harriet got to her feet. "Come along let's eat, I don't know about you but I am famished." Harriet lead the way to a candle lit dining room. The starter was all ready prepared and was keeping warm over a small flame burner. Harriet placed Jerby's plate in front of him. Jerby was rather startled to see the starter was a combination of sausage and black pudding. Harriet poured more red wine, she smiled again the candle light flickering over her pale complexion and revealing once again those perfect teeth. Jerby noticed that Harriet wasn't really eating. "I thought you were famished." Said Jerby. He was feeling rather guilty as he was almost half way through his food and felt as though he should be waiting for his hostess to begin eating. "Oh I'm fine, you carry on, I'll wait to enjoy my main course." Replied Harriet. Harriet rose to her feet. "Excuse me a moment." "Oh yes, yes of course." Jerby continued eating almost as though he had been hypnotised, he couldn't leave his food alone. Harriet left the room. Jerby thought that Harriet had gone to check on the main course. He almost choked when Harriet reappeared wearing a very revealing negligee. Jerby could tell that Harriet had nothing on underneath. "Shall we take our wine up to the bedroom to finish it, I have another bottle up there waiting for us." Jerby spluttered. "Yes." Hardly believing his luck and relieved he had visited the machine in the gents.

Harriet lead the way upstairs to her bedroom. The curtains were almost closed and were of the same material as the red satin bedding. Jerby also noticed that the walls were a shade of scarlet that he had never seen before. Harriet sat on the bed she patted the space beside her. "Come and sit here." Again that wonderful smile. Jerby sat next to Harriet on the bed. Suddenly Jerby felt the old familiar panic when he was alone with a beautiful woman and Harriet was indeed beautiful. "Um won't the main course spoil. Don't you want to wait until later?" Harriet turned towards Jerby smiling yet again that wonderful smile revealing those perfect teeth. That was Jerby's last memory as Harriet sank those perfect white teeth into his neck.

HETTY'S STORY

Seek not too deep the answers for to find,
*   The truth is all around you,*
If you will dare to look,
The answers that you seek shall end in certain death.

The heat was unbearable. Hetty struggled to breathe, the more she struggled the less she could breathe. Breath was now drawn in in ragged gasps, Hetty knew that this was the end, that her life was over. She tried to cry out, to scream for help but no sound came. As Hetty looked up she could see a dark tunnel and as she struggled for breath she was being drawn closer and closer to the tunnel. As Hetty drew closer to the mouth of the tunnel she could see a small pinprick of light, but the voices and the screaming cackles of laughter that had echoed all around her for what seemed like hours became louder and louder. Just as Hetty was about the be drawn into the tunnel, towards certain death she heard a new voice. "Hetty. Hetty. Wake up!" Hetty struggled to go back, back away from the tunnel towards the voice, a voice that she was sure she recognised. "Hetty!" Hetty drew in another ragged breath as she fought her way back. Suddenly with a gasp Hetty opened her eyes and found herself once more in her familiar bedroom with Jack by her side. As usual Hetty was drenched in sweat, her pyjamas sticking to her as she flung her arms around Jack's neck and sobbed uncontrollably when she realised that she was safe. "Was it that same nightmare again?" Asked Jack, though he knew the answer before he had asked the question. "Yes. The same over and over. Oh Jack what does it all mean, why do I keep having this dreadful dream?" "Well you have been overdoing it just lately. You have been working so hard until all hours to seal the deal on that contract for your clients. Now that the deal has been completed perhaps we can settle down and plan that long overdue holiday we have been promising ourselves." Yes of course. As usual Jack had hit the nail on the head. Hetty knew that she had been overworking over the past few months and struggling to switch off. Her mind had been working overtime and so when she had finally fallen into bed she had spent hours tossing and turning, then when she eventually fell asleep overtired and exhausted the nightmare would begin.

The following evening when Jack came home from work Hetty had some exciting news. "I have booked that holiday for us. I checked out a website and this place just popped up, just like it was meant to be. It is a small but perfectly formed cottage in the village of Leystone, South Devon and just exactly what we need. A bit of peace and quiet in the middle of nowhere so we can unwind. There is a small village shop for bits and pieces and a lovely pub and a tearoom. We can go and chill out and just have some lovely walks, good food and few glasses of chilled wine. How does that sound?" Jack smiled, "It sounds idyllic and just what we both need." Jack knew that Hetty had been feeling very guilty of late working all hours and any quality time with Jack had been virtually nil. "When do we go?" "Friday week, for a whole week."

The longed for first day of the holiday dawned clear and bright, the sun shone from an almost cloudless sky and with the car packed Hetty and Jack set off with high hopes for a restful holiday. The trip was faultless and they arrived at Leystone in time for lunch at the pretty little tearoom on the village green which was just opposite to the thatched chocolate box cottage that was to be their base for the next week.

After a long and indulgent lunch Hetty and Jack found the key to Rose Cottage and began to explore. The lounge had a massive inglenook fireplace with a wood burning stove which, as it was high summer they wouldn't need, but they both exclaimed how cosy it would be on cold winter evenings to sit around the fire with a glass or two of something nice. Next they explored the bedroom upstairs. The bed was massive as was the room, they immediately felt as though this would be a restful week away from the hustle and bustle of home and work. Later, after unpacking, Hetty and Jack decided to have a short stroll around the village. The whole place was full of quaint cottages, some thatched as Theirs was, others were plainly very old. The heart of the village was around the green, as the tearoom, pub and church were all centred in that area. Next door to the village of Leystone was the small hamlet of Wayside which was reached by a short walk through a footpath that passed by the front door of Rose Cottage. Wayside was just picture perfect. It was all ancient thatched cottages with the archetypal roses around the door that everyone dreams of owning. Hetty and Jack were in awe of the area, all of the lanes were so narrow they wondered how any vehicles could ever reach the cottages, as for any removal firms they had no idea how they would cope. As they explored the village and hamlet they saw a great number of cars with scrapes and scratches along the sides and were not at all surprised.

It was later that evening when Hetty had climbed into bed exhausted that the she noticed the painting. The painting was of the cottage that they were staying in. It also featured the next door cottage which had a tiny picket gate enclosing a small garden. The cottage that Hetty and Jack were renting had no frontage and just a tiny strip of lawn to the side on which a bench had been placed to soak up the last rays of sun at the end of the day. As Hetty admired the painting she was sure that there was a figure of a women in the tiny porch of their cottage and the figure of a man by the gate of the next door property. Hetty rubbed her eyes, she was so tired she decided that she would take a proper look tomorrow when she was more awake. That night for once Hetty slept peacefully with no nightmares to disturb her or Jack.

The following morning again dawned sunny and clear. Hetty forgot to have another look at the painting as she and Jack planned their day over breakfast. They decided to take a picnic lunch and to spend a day exploring the local countryside around Leystone. After a busy day exploring and a delicious evening meal at the local pub, The Ley, they took a stroll around the village before bed. They decided to take a look at the gravestones in the nearby churchyard. Hetty had been reading up about the history of Leystone the evening before. The leaflet had said that there had been a place of worship on the site for hundreds of years. Historians believed that as the church was surrounded by a round boundary wall the place had Pagan origins.

Whist exploring the gravestones Hetty was surprised to see that several of the graves were of people who bore the same name as her family name, Moreland. Much to Hetty's consternation there was also a grave bearing the name Henrietta Moreland, her name. Hetty felt a shiver run down her spine. The sun was just setting and it was casting long shadows over the graveyard, and in particular the grave of Henrietta Moreland. Jack could see that Hetty was upset, he put his arm around her, "Come on time for a nightcap before bed." Said Jack firmly, leading Hetty towards the cottage. That night again as Hetty climbed into bed she looked at the picture. Yes there was definitely a female figure in the doorway of the cottage and a male figure leaning over the gate of the cottage next door.

The following morning was again warm and sunny and much to Jack's relief Hetty appeared to have forgotten the episode of the previous evening. Once again they made plans for their day over breakfast. They decided to visit a local beauty spot on the high moors above Leystone and then do whatever the day unfolded. As they reached their destination they saw a stone circle and a little way away from it there was a tall standing stone which cast long shadows over the moors. As they were exploring the stones a woman walking her dog appeared. "Good morning." Said Hetty and Jack. "Do you live in the area?" The woman stopped. "Oh yes my dears I have lived here in the area all of my long life." "Please could you tell us a little about the stones?" Asked Jack. "Ah well this is the place where they used to worship the Ancient Gods and make human sacrifice if it was deemed necessary. That there," Continued the lady inclining her head towards the very tall standing stone, "Was where they would await their fate, it's called the Leystone. There is a village not far away by the same name. It is rumoured to be haunted by the ghosts of witches put to death here and in the village during the witch trials. Terrible times they were, some of my distant ancestors were put to death on the village green at Leystone." Hetty and Jack were rather taken aback by this and couldn't find any words to say. "Well good day to you both." At this the woman, calling to her dog went on her way.

With the woman's words ringing in their ears they decided that it was time to leave the stones to themselves and to return to Leystone for some lunch. After lunch Hetty and Jack sat on the grass outside their cottage. Much to their surprise the same woman appeared, once again with her dog. "Hello again." Began Jack. "Oh hello my dears, I had no idea that you were staying here in Leystone in this cottage." The woman introduced herself as Joan. "What a coincidence I should see you up at the stones this morning. I was born in this cottage, my family owned it for many years as they owned most of the cottages and houses around the Village Green and also the cottages at Wayside just along the lane. My family go back generations in Leystone." Hetty and Jack were fascinated to hear the story and also the history of the cottage they were staying in. They were also surprised to hear that what appeared to be a very small cottage attached to theirs, was in fact, much larger and at one time had been part of the cottage they were renting. "Oh yes my father put in an extra bedroom and then the cottages were divided up. The wall in the built in wardrobe in the main bedroom of Rose Cottage was at one point the way through to the next door cottage but it was blocked up years ago to form the cottages as you see them now. So we had Rose Cottage where you are staying, next door is Bluebell Cottage and that one," Joan intimated the cottage with the small garden and picket gate, "Is Buttercup Cottage."

"So you know lots of history of the village?" Asked Hetty, thinking at once of the trip the previous evening to the churchyard and the graves they had seen. "Oh yes my dear, as

I said my family have lived here generations. The Morelands built Leystone and Wayside." Hetty couldn't believe her ears. "Sorry did you say your name was Moreland?" "Yes of course it is." Replied Joan. "My maiden name before I married was Moreland, it's Henrietta Moreland and this is my Husband Jack." Just then the sun disappeared behind a cloud and both Joan and Hetty shivered. "Turning chilly my dears, time I was going."

That evening when Hetty was preparing for bed she thought that she could smell smoke in the bedroom, Hetty sniffed again, yes it was definitely smoke. Hetty went to the open window to look out to see if anyone had a bonfire but as she closed the window there was nothing to see.

Hetty remembered that she had planned to have a closer look at the painting to check out who the figures were in the picture but, when Hetty looked closely there was no one to be seen. "That's very strange." She said to herself, "I was sure that there was a woman in the porch of this cottage, must be a trick of the light or the angle the picture is hanging."

That night Hetty had the nightmare yet again. This time it seemed even worse than usual, Jack had to comfort her for a very long time before she finally fell into a fitful sleep once more.

Hetty woke with a dreadful headache, she felt hungover and ill after the nightmare. Jack made her tea and toast and insisted Hetty remained in bed until she had finished it. As Hetty was eating her breakfast she glanced towards the painting. The figure of the woman and man were back, so she hadn't imagined it. "Jack, Jack!" Cried Hetty. Jack rushed into the bedroom. "What's the matter?" Asked Jack in alarm. "Look at the picture and tell me what you see." Commanded Hetty. Jack looked at the picture. "Well I see a painting of this cottage, the one adjoining it that Joan was telling us about and the next door cottage with the small front garden." "Yes, what else can you see. Can you see any figures in the painting?" Demanded Hetty. Jack looked again, "Well yes I think I can see what you mean, but I think it's just a trick of the light or something or it's just your headache affecting your eyesight." "No, no the figures come and go. I checked last evening before I got into bed and there was definitely nothing there, but this morning and on other occasions I have seen a figure of a woman and a man." Jack turned to look at Hetty. "Are you sure you are feeling OK after last night and it's not just your eyes playing tricks?"

"Yes I am feeling much better and another thing when I was getting ready for bed last night I could smell smoke in here." Jack was beginning to feel really concerned now. Were the nightmares a symptom of something else, was Hetty on the verge of a breakdown. She had been so stressed of late, he decided that if things continued like this a visit to their GP was a must when they got home. "Come on then if you are feeling better, it's a gorgeous day again lets get out and about and explore Dartmouth it's not far away."

Dartmouth was warm and sunny. The sun sparkled on the river as Hetty and Jack sat in Bayard's Cove enjoying a fish and chip lunch. The gulls eyed their food hungrily, occasionally scrapping amongst themselves to decide who would be first in line for any leftovers. "Go away, we have eaten it all." Said Jack laughing as he collected up the wrappings and placed them in the gull proof bin.

They enjoyed a pleasant afternoon browsing around the shops in the tiny narrow streets where they bought a few mementoes of their visit.

When they arrived back at Leystone Hetty noticed that the village archive in the church was open. "Oh lets go and have a look." Cried Hetty, "I would love to find out more about the village and it's history. With a sinking feeling Jack followed Hetty towards the church.

"Welcome, welcome." Greeted the custodian. "Can I help you with anything?" "Well yes I am interested in finding out more about Rose Cottage." Replied Hetty, pointing to where they were staying. "And also about the Moreland family." "Ah yes," Said Katy, the custodian. "If you follow me I can point you in the right direction. If you can't find out everything you need today there is an excellent website that features the history of Leystone, and in particular, the Moreland family who were responsible for building most of the village and Wayside just along the lane."

Hetty and Jack followed Katy to the far corner of the archive room where they saw several shelves dedicated to the Moreland family. "Thank you so much." Said Hetty. "No problem at all. If I can help with anything else just give me a call."

The rest of the afternoon rushed by. Soon it was time to leave the archive room as it was closing up for the day. As Hetty left the church to return to Rose Cottage her mind was buzzing with information she must share with Jack. Jack had left some time ago, citing that a beer at the pub was called for as it had turned into such a hot day. Hetty tried to make sense of what she had been reading and before she left the churchyard she revisited Henrietta Moreland's grave, she wanted to read the inscription properly.

Henrietta Moreland
Born 3rd April 1658
Died August 3rd 1685
Thy sins shall follow ye to thy grave
Cast out thy evil spirits
Follow the ways of the Lord

Hetty shivered. It felt as though something cold had touched her even though the sun was still shining warmly, but this area of the churchyard seemed to be in permanent shadow. Hetty glimpsed a movement and turned quickly, it was Jack. "Hi. I came to see if you were on your way back to the cottage." Said Jack. Hetty turned to face Jack, her face pale. "What is it, has your headache come back?" Asked Jack full of concern. "No, no it's not that. I have found out some very interesting stuff this afternoon, lets go back to Rose Cottage and over a cuppa

I will fill you in." Hetty would say no more until the tea was made and they had both eaten a piece of delicious cake that they had bought from the tearoom opposite.

"Well?" Inquired Jack. "It seems that this village and several of the cottages in it and Wayside were the site of several witch trials. Rose Cottage in particular was involved and Henrietta Moreland was named as one of the witches. I looked at her grave again before I left the churchyard and it says something about sins and evil spirits. The date fits too." "Well that is interesting." Said Jack. "There is more," Replied Hetty. "It seems that the cottage next door was occupied by a family by the name of Knight and they had a son named Jack. Hetty and Jack were, I think, lovers the old manuscripts were pretty coy in the wording but I think so." Hetty waited for all of this to sink in then went on. "I think this is why I am here, why I have been having all of the nightmares. I think it is Hetty and Jack in the painting. I think I have to do something about it." Jack turned to Hetty, his face grim. "No! This is utter nonsense. You have finally lost it. All of the strain you have been under recently has unbalanced you. We need to get you to a doctor as soon as possible when we go home. This holiday was supposed to be a rest. Time for us to unwind and spend some time together for once, not for you to be meddling in things you do not understand and are well and truly history!" Hetty couldn't believe her ears. She faced Jack, tears streaming down her cheeks. "But it all fits. I think we should go and find Joan and ask her more about this cottage and Buttercup Cottage to find out the truth. Then perhaps I shall settle and the nightmares will end and we can get on with our lives. Perhaps start the family we have been putting off and putting off. Please Jack." Jack knew deep down that Hetty was right, that this Thing would never go away unless they explored it further. That Hetty would never settle until they found out the full facts. "We will find out where Joan lives tomorrow and pay her a visit first thing." Said Jack, "In the meantime supper and bed."

That night as Hetty was undressing she could smell smoke

even worse than the previous evening, the acrid stench filled the bedroom and made Hetty's eyes water. Hetty went to the painting and yes both figures were there. Henrietta and Jack were both there. Was it her imagination or were they now both facing her with a look of pleading on their faces? Hetty rubbed her eyes and checked the painting again, no this time Henrietta and Jack were as before looking at one another.

That night, yet again Hetty and Jack's sleep was disturbed by Hetty's screams and sobs. The following morning Jack was up and about before Hetty was awake. He paid a visit to the village shop to buy bacon and eggs and to enquire where Joan lived. Armed with breakfast and Joan's address Jack returned to Rose Cottage to find Hetty was awake and dressed.

After breakfast they made their way to Joan's cottage, it was up the lane in the hamlet of Wayside. When they rang the bell they were greeted by barking so they knew that Joan must be at home and not out on one of her daily walks.

"Oh, hello its you." Greeted Joan when she opened the door. "I wondered how long it would be before you came to find me. Come in and I will put the kettle on. Go through to the garden with Monty its such a lovely day, too nice to be indoors." Hetty and Jack, accompanied by Monty the dog, made their way into the lovely garden.

"So," Began Joan when everyone had been served coffee and cake. "You want to know more about Rose Cottage and Henrietta Moreland?" Hetty gasped. "How did you know that is what we came to see you about?" Asked Hetty. "Well my dear, I saw you come out of the archive yesterday and I also saw how upset you were after your visit to the graveyard. I guessed that you had seen Henrietta's grave and as you share the same name I felt sure that you would be upset." "Not only the same name but we share the same birthday." Replied Hetty. "Ah, yes I can understand how this would make you feel." Said Joan sympathetically. "Now drink up your coffee and I will tell you the story." Hetty and Jack meekly did as they were told. "Now," Continued Joan. "As I told you a few days ago my family has been in Leystone for generations, they built all the older part of the village and some of the newer parts. By that I don't mean the modern houses but the older style houses. Over the years the houses and cottages have been sold off to other families, some to long standing villagers others to incomers, but as I say all now sold off. The cottage you are staying in belonged to Henrietta's family and Buttercup Cottage was rented to Jack Knight's family. Henrietta's mother was the village Midwife and Wise Woman and she made up various salves and potions from herbs that grow in and around the village. When Henrietta's mother died the role passed on to Henrietta as was the normal thing in those days. Henrietta had helped her mother deliver countless babies over the years and helped her gather the herbs she needed to make the salves and potions. Jack Knight's family had lived in Buttercup Cottage for many years. Jack and Henrietta grew up together and as is often the way of these things they started courting and were going to get married." "Then it is them in the painting!" Exclaimed Hetty. Joan paused. "What painting?" Hetty explained about the painting hanging in the bedroom at Rose Cottage. "And you see the figures of Henrietta and Jack keep appearing and disappearing and almost moving around." Finished Hetty. "Well in that case you may have seen the old rhyme in the archives.

> *Seek not too deep the answers for to find,*
> *The truth is all around you,*
> *If you will dare to look,*
> *The answers that you seek shall end in certain death."*

Hetty shuddered. "No I hadn't seen it. What does it mean?" "It is an old saying about Rose Cottage and the truth about Henrietta, and of course, her death." "Her death, how did she die. I saw that she was quite young when she died, about my age now." Said Hetty.

Joan continued with her story. "As I said Henrietta and Jack were to be married, the bans had been read and all was going ahead when things started to go wrong. Several of the village children became ill and a few mothers died in childbirth and several cows miscarried. Tongues began to wag and fingers were pointed at Henrietta. After all she was the village Midwife and Wise Woman and she attended to everyone and mixed up the medicines. The local Vicar involved the Bishop and the magistrates and before long the term "Witch" was being bandied about. At the time it was at the height of the persecution of witches and the witch trials and Henrietta was made a scape goat for everything that had gone wrong in the village. Of course it was probably some form of virus or bacteria but in those days these things had not been heard of so Henrietta was blamed. Henrietta was going to be tried by the Magistrate but before that could happen the villagers took matters into their own hands." Hetty looked at Jack. They both knew what was coming next. "They burnt her didn't they?" Asked Hetty in a small voice. "Yes my dear they did. The night before the trial the villagers rioted outside Rose Cottage and when Henrietta refused to come out they set fire to the cottage." Hetty felt cold and Jack put his arm around her. "So that is why I have been having all of those nightmares and why I felt so drawn to Leystone and Rose Cottage." Whispered Hetty. Joan gave Hetty a sharp look. "You certainly seem to have the gift of Sight." Said Joan. "I am not sure about destiny or whatever you may call it, but yes, I feel that you could have been drawn here as you phrase it. Certainly I do not believe that there is such a thing as a coincidence, everything happens for a reason."

"So what does the rhyme mean?" Asked Hetty. "Well. When Rose Cottage was set on fire Jack tried to save Henrietta. He ran to the side of the building to see if he could climb in a window but he couldn't get in. Eventually he managed to smash the window and climbed in to find Henrietta, but it was too late Henrietta was already dead. What today we would call smoke inhalation had got to her. When Jack carried Henrietta out of the cottage dead but not a mark on her, her fate was sealed and she was branded a Witch. There and then they set upon the corpse and cut out Henrietta's heart and ran it through with

Hawthorn twigs. They bound it in some of Henrietta's hair and put it in a pouch and hid it in the cottage as a protection charm and a warning to others not to practice Witchcraft." "Where did they hide the pouch. Was it ever found?" Asked Jack. "Well I believe it was hidden somewhere by the fireplace but I am not sure, and anyway, with alterations being done over the years it would never be found now. Why do you ask?" "Because I am plagued by nightmares that I am in a fire and can't breathe and I am going to die, then Jack saves me. All the while I can hear taunting laughter." Hetty began to shake and sob. "I must be here for a reason. Perhaps I am supposed to find this pouch, but if I find it what should I do with it?"

"If you find the pouch you will need to bury it in Henrietta's grave at midnight at a full moon. There is a full moon tomorrow night."

Hetty and Jack stood up. "Thank you for so much of your time. Our course of action is now clear, to stop the nightmares we must see if we can find the pouch and then bury it to reunite Henrietta with her heart so that she and Jack may at long last rest in peace. But before we go please answer this. If Henrietta was branded a Witch how come she was buried in sacred ground in the churchyard?"

"Ah well you forget that Henrietta's family were very powerful. They threatened to evict all of the tenants and the vicar if Henrietta was not buried in the churchyard. The vicar and villagers had to agree but Henrietta is not buried in the same plot as the rest of the Moreland family she is in an overgrown shaded area that never sees any sun and her gravestone urges her to repent her sins." "Yes I had noticed that." Said Hetty "I did wonder why she was not with the rest of the family and the area was so cold and miserable. What happened to Jack?" Asked Hetty. "Jack suffered severe burns when he tried to rescue Henrietta and they presumably became infected, either way he died within a few weeks of Henrietta and is buried in the churchyard too."

Jack and Hetty walked back to Rose Cottage in silence,

each absorbed in their own thoughts. *"Seek not too deep the answers for to find."* Kept going round and round in Hetty's mind. *"The answers that you seek shall end in certain death."* Was in Jack's thoughts. Did this mean that if this wasn't all sorted out that Hetty would be driven slowly mad and that she would die. He just couldn't think straight. He knew one thing, they must turn the cottage upside down to find the answers and then they may just be able to carry on with their lives.

The first place Jack and Hetty looked was the most obvious, the fireplace. They hadn't realised how massive it was until they began to check it out. They checked every brick at the front of the fireplace and all around the wood burner. They felt sure if the pouch had been discovered when the wood burner had been put in it would be common knowledge. Next they climbed onto the base of the grate where the logs could be stored and they could look directly up the chimney and check the wooden lintel from behind and all of the bricks as high as they could reach. They fetched a stool to stand on so they could reach even higher but nothing was to be found.

Next they went up to the bedroom as the chimney ran up the wall and through the bedroom to the chimney stack on the roof. They tapped the walls to see if there was any false wall but it was all solid. They opened the large cupboard in the bedroom to see if there were any false bits of wall or floor boards but found nothing. "I just don't know where else to look," Said Jack. "If Joan's father rebuilt this even sixty years ago the pouch would have been found. We are talking over three hundred years since the pouch was hidden. It has probably rotted to nothing by now or someone found it during renovations and threw it away or gave it to the museum at Boscastle."

They went downstairs both of them thinking about the rhyme.

Seek not too deep the answers for to find,
The truth is all around you,

If you will dare to look,
The answers that you seek shall end in certain death."

"What does the rhyme mean. We need to go through it logically." Reasoned Hetty. *"Seek not too deep,"* perhaps that means the answer is on the surface and not buried. *"The truth is all around you.* Does that mean it is under our very noses and we can't find it or see it?"

"Dare to look." Said Jack. Neither of them wanted to think about the last line of the rhyme especially after what Joan had told them and Hetty's nightmares. Both were afraid that the end would be Hetty's death.

"This cottage has been renovated many times over the past years. The current owners have done a fair amount of work. Look the floor has been relaid and I am sure I read somewhere that it has underfloor heating. If the pouch was there it would either have been found or buried under the floor and no way am I going to be responsible for digging up the floors." Said Jack. "Let's check out the fireplace again." Once again they checked and rechecked the fireplace and the great wooden beam that ran over the top of the lintel. Nothing. They both sat in despair, defeat etched on their faces. Suddenly Jack exclaimed. "The cottages. This one and Bluebell next door were once one large cottage and certainly would have been when Henrietta and Jack were alive. Is the pouch in there, is the pouch in or under the fireplace in Bluebell?"

"How do we find out who owns the cottage, I have never seen anyone in there? Yes of course Joan will know!" Cried Hetty. At that moment they heard a huge crash and splintering of glass. They rushed upstairs, the painting had fallen off the wall and lay on the bedroom floor, shards of glass all around. Hetty had gone very pale. "What is it?" Began Jack, then he looked to where Hetty was pointing. There, a little way from the main scene of devastation was a large shard of broken glass in the shape of an arrow pointing towards the wardrobe doors. "I think we may be on the right track." Said Jack.

Hetty and Jack hastened to Joan's cottage. When Joan answered the door they were both so breathless they could hardly speak. "Now, now calm yourselves down and explain what you need my dears." Said Joan. "The pouch, Bluebell Cottage, the pouch." Gasped Jack. "Come away in and sit and tell me slowly." Said Joan ushering them inside her cottage and through to the garden. When they were sitting calmly with a glass of lemonade each Joan listened to their theory. "Well yes you could just be right." Replied Joan. "Bluebell has had very little done to it over the years. I am not saying it is as it was all those years ago but my family did little to it and the current owners use it rarely. Certainly there is little in the way of modernisation inside." "Please do you know who owns Bluebell or who may have a key so that we can check it out?" Asked Hetty, determined now to see this through to the end in the hope that her nightmares would end. "Well I have a key, the owner is my very distant cousin and as I said she uses it very rarely these days and it is in a bit of a state inside, but I am sure that you can borrow the key and have a look if it will put your mind at rest." "Thank you, thank you." Said Hetty and Jack together. "I will just get the key." Joan went back inside the cottage and soon returned with the key to Bluebell Cottage. "Here you are my dears. Take your time and lock up securely when you have finished." Hetty and Jack thanked Joan and hurried back to Bluebell Cottage. Jack fitted the key into the lock and took a deep breath as he slowly opened the door. Both Hetty and Jack were transfixed. It was like stepping back in time. Bluebell Cottage was like something from a living museum. The walls were plain whitewash and the original flagstones were on the floor. The kitchen had an ancient range cooker and an old scrubbed wooden table. The old sink had lead pipes and a single tap with a scrubbed wooden draining board and there was one free standing storage unit come larder. "Goodness, its like the land time forgot." Exclaimed Hetty. "How has this survived like this until the twenty first century, I can't quite believe what I am seeing." Jack stood beside her speechless. "But you know what this means," continued Hetty. "It means we may just find what we are looking for." "But where to start?" "Upstairs." Hetty followed Jack as he lead the way upstairs to the upper floors. "Remember the glass arrow." Said Jack. "It was pointing towards the wardrobe doors. That is where the two cottages were divided many years ago. It stands to reason that the pouch is here somewhere, lets start upstairs in the bedrooms and then make our way downstairs. We need to be methodical about this. It is the full moon tomorrow, if you are going to bury the pouch at midnight we need to find it."

The bedrooms were almost as untouched as the downstairs. There was an indoor bathroom that looked as though it had been installed in the early part of the twentieth century, a huge cast iron bath, gigantic washbasin and a toilet with a high mounted cistern. "Wow. Another museum piece." Said Jack. "After a thorough check of the bathroom Hetty and Jack headed towards the bedrooms, in particular the one that adjoined Rose Cottage. Nothing. They searched and searched. They tapped walls and the plain floorboards, there were a couple of small mats to move but no carpets anywhere in the whole property. Nothing. As they went back downstairs they checked the staircase and the risers to see if any loose boards hid the pouch. Again nothing. After a thorough check of the kitchen and flagstone floors they turned their attention to the parlour, in no way could it be described as a lounge. They checked every flagstone, lifting the small rug in front of the huge fireplace. They tapped the walls again. Nothing. Then for the fireplace. Hetty and Jack both climbed onto the hearth so they could check all around the back of the fire and the huge lintel. Nothing. Suddenly right at the back of the fireplace Jack saw a large space. "An old bread oven." Said Jack. Quickly Hetty rushed to the space. She checked all around the base and sides of the oven. She tapped all of the stones and then Hetty began to search above the opening to the oven. She felt all around it with her hands, suddenly she could feel a ledge above the opening to the oven, something was there, Hetty let out a scream as a huge cobweb and spider fell onto the base of the oven. Followed by a filthy leather pouch. Hetty and Jack looked at one another then back at the pouch. "This is it." Whispered Hetty. Hardly daring to breathe Hetty gingerly picked up the pouch scarcely daring to touch it. "Shall I open it?" "Yes, yes open it." Said Jack struggling to stop himself from snatching it from Hetty's hand. Carefully Hetty opened the pouch. Inside was small piece of twig pushed through a desiccated piece of leather which at some point may have been a human heart. Around the heart were several strands of once blond hair. "This is it," Whispered Hetty once again, it was almost as though she dare not speak too loudly. "We have found it." Tears of sadness mingled with joy flowed from both Hetty and Jack as they embraced. Jack uttered a sigh of relief. Perhaps now all of Hetty's nightmares would end and she would be back to her old self once more. Hopefully they could now begin to think about the family they both wanted.

They made their way back to Rose Cottage. Once inside Hetty carefully placed the pouch on the chest of drawers in the bedroom whilst they tidied up the mess of glass and painting. Once the glass had all been removed from the frame they rehung the painting on the wall. They would contact the owner of Rose Cottage to explain about the broken glass and even though they had not caused the damage they would offer to pay for a new piece of glass.

That night Hetty slept through with no nightmares. The following day dawned once again clear and bright. Tonight was the full moon. The night when Hetty must bury the pouch in Henrietta's grave so that the nightmares would cease and Henrietta and her heart would be complete once more.

They passed the day quietly with some gentle strolls around the village and a light lunch at the cafe, both Hetty and Jack felt too nervous to eat much. They checked out the churchyard and found that the shed containing the groundsman's tools was never locked so they would have access to a shovel when they needed it.

That evening they watched the sunset knowing that within a few short hours they would be completing their task. At a twenty to midnight they left Rose Cottage and made their way carefully and quietly to the churchyard and by the light of a shaded torch beam they selected a shovel from the tool shed. Then they walked reverently to Henrietta's grave. As the church clock began to strike midnight Jack put the shovel into the ground. As it was summer they had expected the ground to be rock hard but the soil gave easily and before very long Jack had dug a reasonably deep hole above where they judged Henrietta's heart would be. Carefully Hetty placed the pouch inside the newly dug hole. They both stood there in quiet reflection as they waited for the clock to stop striking. Hetty had written a short prayer which she whispered.

Henrietta, may you now rest in peace, we return your heart to it's rightful place. Blessings be with you on this midsummer night. Rest easy now beneath the earth in this sacred place.

Then, as is usual at most burials, both Hetty and Jack picked up a handful of earth and placed it over the pouch before Jack filled in the rest of the grave. As they finished they both felt a huge weight lift from their shoulders. Quietly they returned the shovel to the shed and then walked slowly back to Rose Cottage.

The following day was the last of their holiday. At last they felt rested and calm. Jack especially noticed a big change in Hetty. Gone were the dark shadows under her eyes and she seemed light hearted and at peace.

For several days after Hetty and Jack arrived home they pondered what the rhyme had fully meant.

Seek not too deep the answers for to find,
The truth is all around you,
If you will dare to look,
The answers that you seek shall end in certain death."

The first three lines were really self explanatory it was the last line they couldn't work out. They didn't have to look too deeply and the answer and truth when they had at last figured it out with Joan's help was also fairly obvious. It was the "Shall end in certain death." They puzzled over, then suddenly the answer to that riddle became obvious too. "Shall end in certain death." It is Henrietta's death, her final resting at peace. Nothing sinister, it is not my death." Said a very relieved Hetty. Jack smiled as he took Hetty in his arms, he too had reached that conclusion. "Now about that family we are planning."

Postscript; I did some research. The last person executed for Witchcraft in Devon was in 1685

A HEDGEROW STORY

Marti shivered. She had been sitting here for hours or was it days, weeks, months she had no idea as everything looked and felt the same. Once again Marti went over in her mind what had happened. She had been walking along the lane to her friend Patty's house to just hang out and listen to music when everything had gone so badly wrong. She remembered that she had just finished eating a Mars bar and a packet of crisps for her breakfast, when next thing she knew, she was in this cold horrid dank place. She had felt what seemed to be strong and rough hands grab her from nowhere and then nothing until she had woken up here. Suddenly, she heard it, an unmistakable rustling sound. She strained her ears to listen. What was it? Marti had thoughts of rats, mice, cockroaches, worms and slugs. Whatever it was Marti was sure it was cold, disgusting and slimy. After a while there seemed to be a glimmer of light in the gloom. As she looked around Marti could make out what seemed to be tree roots covered in thick dark green moss and as she looked the moss seemed to be moving. Yes. Yes it was moving. As Marti stared at the moss long bony fingers with long pointed filthy finger nails appeared around one of the roots. "Hello, who are you? Please help me." Croaked Marti, suddenly aware that she had not had anything to eat or drink for ages. As soon as she had spoken the hand had disappeared and once again Marti was left in the gloomy half light. Marti began to cry. She could feel wet tears on her cheeks, she brushed them away before looking at her hands and then realised that her hands were covered in soil and mud. "Oh I must look a real mess," Said Marti to herself, tears flowing even harder now. Marti lifted up the edge of her hoodie to wipe her face hoping that it would be less muddy than her hands. Marti felt her hair. It was sticking up everywhere and seemed to be covered in leaves and bits of old tree roots and bark. She tried to comb it with her fingers then realised that she was just making it look even worse. "Oh what is the point no one can see me down here." Marti thought miserably to herself. Marti then began to think about Patty. Would she be worried about her, would she just think that Marti had decided not to come round, would she try to phone or text. "Oh I am an idiot!" Exclaimed Marti. Phone! She fumbled in her pockets for her phone, the one thing she had totally forgotten about. The thing that she could use to make contact with the outside world, the thing that would brighten up this gloomy dark place. All pockets well and truly searched, not a sign of her phone. Next Marti felt all around the area she was sitting in.....nothing. The hot salty tears flowed once again. Where was she, why had no one come to her aid, who was the owner of the long bony fingers?

Marti must have dozed off for it seemed a long while later that she heard more sounds. Marti also realised that she was by now very thirsty and hungry. The space she was in was also getting quite smelly. She had needed to empty her bladder a couple of times, she had done it a fair way from where she was sitting but even so it wasn't at all nice. She had a horrid thought, what about when she needed to do more than just a wee. Yuk thought Marti with a shudder.

The sounds began to be louder, there was definitely something or someone approaching. Remembering the last time Bony Fingers had appeared Marti decided to keep quiet to see who it was. Again the bony fingers and disgusting nails moved the moss to one side and a smallish bent man walked towards her. "Awake now are you?" Asked the man. "Well yes. As I am sure you can see." Retorted Marti. "Can I go home now, my mother and my friend will wonder where I am and be very worried. If you don't let me go you will be in terrible trouble with the Police when I do get home." "Well you are in a tantrum aren't you." Replied Bony Fingers. "Just wait until the Boss meets you." Bony Fingers cackled in glee. "The Boss, who is the Boss?" "Oh you just wait and see. He will want you to come and share supper soon, meanwhile you just bide there until I come for you."

At this Marti wasn't at all sure if she wanted to meet The Boss, though the thought of some food and drink was enticing and her stomach rumbled even more at the thought of it.

After a while Marti again heard sounds of someone approaching. Once again the bony hand was the first thing to appear around the tree roots. Bony Fingers beckoned to Marti. "Follow me it is this way." Marti stood up to follow Bony Fingers. She was stiff and sore and was aware how filthy and smelly she was. I hope The Boss had a cold thought Marti. I stink.

Bony Fingers lead Marti through a maze of tunnels and tree roots until they arrived at what could only be described as an underground banqueting chamber. Small lights glittered everywhere on the walls and an appetising smell of food drifted on the air. Bony Fingers led Marti to a chair next to what almost appeared to be a throne. "Sit." Commanded Bony Fingers. Marti sat down a feeling of dizziness creeping over her, partly because of hunger, and partly because of the deep fear and trepidation she felt.

Suddenly Bony Fingers moved away from Marti and bowed. Marti looked towards a doorway and saw someone approaching. The man was dressed in brown from head to toe and his shoulder length hair was the colour of horse chestnuts. "Ah Marti I believe?" Said the man who Marti now assumed to be The Boss. "Yes," replied Marti, "Please may I go home now?" "Home. I don't think so, not until you have had the benefit of our hospitality for a good while longer." Marti could feel the tears rolling down her cheeks uncontrollably again. "But I am cold and hungry and have been gone for hours or days, my Mother will be worried, she will have told the police I am missing. Please, please can I go home?"

"Come sit have some food." Said the Boss. With that Bony Fingers clapped his hands and many servants entered the chamber bearing platters of food. Marti's stomach rumbled again and despite her fears realised that she was so very hungry. There were platters of mushrooms, watercress soup, green stuffs and fruits, strawberries, redcurrants and blackcurrants. These were all placed in front of the Boss. "And now a special platter for our guest I think." Said Bony Fingers, "Ah yes here it comes." A wooden platter was placed in front of Marti and the cover was removed. The food looked very strange it was a mix of vibrant colours. Orange, lime, blue, turquoise and something that looked almost opaque, it was all covered in a dark green slime. "But what is this, I can't eat this." Marti stuttered using the spoon from her place at the table to poke and prod the platter. "But why not?" Asked the Boss. "It is something that we find everyday in trees, hedges, fields, streams, rivers and ditches. We have heard from our cousins the Mermen and Mermaids and Dolphins, Sharks, Whales and Turtles that it is also in the deep vast seas and mighty rivers. Please explain why you cannot eat it. I am interested to hear."

"Well because it's not real food it is what we pack or wrap our food in, the real food is inside it. That is the stuff we eat, not this, we throw this away."

"Ah you throw this away. Where does it go when you throw it away?" "Well in the bin and then to the tip, and, and…..." Tailed off Marti, not at all sure what did happen after that. Then Marti had a sudden thought. "Oh, we do recycling." "What is recycling?" "Recycling is when we put some of the rubbish in a special bin and then the council workers take it away." "So tell me what things are recycled in the Special Bin the Council Worker takes away." "Oh glass bottles and plastic bottles and paper and cardboard and tin cans, stuff like that, it's supposed to help the environment." "So what happens next?" Marti was somewhat confused by this question. "I don't know what you mean." Said Marti. "I mean where does this recycling go, where does it end up, what happens to it." Marti then realised that she had absolutely no idea where the rubbish did go." "I don't know." Muttered Marti.

"I shall tell you." Replied The Boss "The rubbish that is recycled often gets taken thousands of miles away from here on big boats which spew out lots of pollutants. If the weather is very stormy the rubbish, which is mostly plastics, gets lost overboard and ends up in the Seas and Oceans of the World. Plastic bags and bag remnants look much like a jellyfish to a turtle so the turtle eats the plastics and then it blocks it's stomach and the turtle dies. Whales, dolphins, basking sharks all eat copious amounts of plastics every year and then this blocks their stomachs and they die a very long and painful death. They starve to death. All of this from your so called recycling and using plastics to wrap your so called Real Food. Marti was stunned. "But I had no idea that this was happening. Is happening."

"So tell me what were you doing just before I had you bought here?" "You had me bought here!" Marti could feel that she was becoming increasingly angry. "You. You bought me here. But why what have I done to be dragged here?" "Think. Think back, what were you doing just before you were bought here."

Marti sat and thought. "Well I was walking to my friend Patty's house and I had just eaten a Mar's bar and a packet of crisps, the next thing I knew I was here." Marti suddenly realised what she had done after she had eaten the chocolate and the crisps, she bowed her head and mumbled, "I threw the rubbish in the hedge." "Exactly. You threw the rubbish in the hedge. What about all of the other times you have thrown rubbish in the hedge, in the lanes, in the fields or on the ground. Don't you realise how much damage you are doing, the wildlife you are damaging or killing with your plastics and other rubbish?" The Boss clapped his hands, Bony Fingers appeared with a black dish full of water which he placed on the table in front of Marti. "Do not touch the water. Sit and look in the water and tell me what you see." Commanded The Boss.

Marti sat looking at the water, at first she could see nothing then, as if a mist had lifted Marti could make out a tabby cat. The cat was walking along a hedge line sniffing and being inquisitive as cats are. Suddenly the cat came upon an empty crisp packet, curious and looking for crumbs the cat's head disappeared further and further into the crisp bag. After a while the cat stopped moving, its breathing becoming fainter and fainter. Marti gasped, tears beginning to stream down her cheeks. "Oh no!" As Marti watched unable to tear herself away from the vision of the dying cat a pair of strong hands appeared, they grasped the cat with one hand and with the other quickly removed the crisp bag from the cat's head. The hands then began to massage the cat's chest, suddenly the cat shook it's head and leapt from the arms of it's rescuer and then ran away over the fields and disappeared. Marti drew a deep breath. The cat had looked so much like her own Mr Tibbs.

"I see that you saw a vision in our mirror." Said The Boss softly. Marti nodded her head. "Yes," she whispered. "I see also that it has made you think and question yourself, this is all for the good. For what you saw happens everyday within the wild landscape all over this beautiful Planet. What was once pristine wilderness is now becoming more and more polluted. What was once clear seas teaming with wildlife and fish is now polluted, all with your plastics, cans and bottles. Ask yourself these questions. Do you need that packet of crisps, bottle of water or coke. Do you need to take that flight to somewhere sunny to then just sit around a pool all day. Do you need that second or third car. Yes, you can only drive one car at a time but what about the raping of Our Mother to get the resources to build the cars? Ah yes I see that you are now beginning to understand why you were bought here."

Marti nodded, she could at last really understand why she had been bought to this place. She was beginning to understand what humans are doing to our wonderful World. That indeed there is no Planet B as she had seen many times on waving placards when the news had been on television. Marti hadn't taken any notice as she was far too busy on her smartphone to think or bother about it. "Yes I understand at last." Whispered Marti.

"Then go. Go now and begin to look at your life in a different light. Organise litter picks, tell your friends, observe nature, look at the beauty all around you. A new emerging bulb or leaf in Spring, the wonder of the trees in high Summer, the harvest and leaves turning golden in the Autumn. It is all there just on your doorstep, no need to travel here and there to witness Nature in all of Her glory.

Marti felt the strong hands lift her from her seat and push her roughly away. Suddenly Marti was once again in the hedge lined lane. Marti looked down and saw that her clothes and hands were clean and unstained. Quickly Marti began to head home. Suddenly Marti stopped. Something was moving in the hedgerow, struggling and then it became very quiet. "No!" Marti rushed towards where Mr Tibbs was lying unconscious by the side of the hedge. Quickly Marti picked up Mr Tibbs and tore the crisp packet from his face. Marti massaged Mr Tibbs chest, Mr Tibbs shook his head and looked up at her and began to purr very loudly, a knowing look on his face. Marti wiped the tears from her eyes and ran her fingers through her hair, as she did so hedgerow leaves fell to the ground.

I was inspired to write this story by a true event that happened to me a few years ago. I was out walking our dog around Axbridge reservoir when a couple called to me that a cat was stuck in a field with its head inside an empty crisp packet. The farmer had put barbed wire along and above the top of the field gate and they couldn't get into the field to free the cat which they knew was dying before their eyes. Me being a skinny thing could get through the cross bars of the gate so I asked the couple to look after the dog whilst I freed the cat which after a while made it's way off across the field. Certainly at least one of it's nine lives used.

A GRANNIE'S MAGICAL STORY

What is Magic? This is a big question and one I tried to answer for our Granddaughter when she came to stay with us.

Maisie is really excited to think, as far as we know, that she is the only child at her school to have a Grannie and Grandad who are Witches, or at least follow a Pagan Wiccan Path. This in my case, involves when needed, some spell work and of course we hold rituals and celebrations eight times throughout the year to honour Nature and the Goddess and the God.

Maisie asked me if I could do real magic and I said. "Yes I could." Eyes almost popping out of her head she was keen to know more. To most children, and Maisie is no exception, magic is the kind of magic performed on television or in films such as Harry Potter. I explained to Maisie that was not real magic it was illusion and camera tricks and just pure fiction.

I went on to explain that the kind of everyday magic I perform is the type of magic everyone can do. Which, as I also explained to her is totally different from spell work, that is when the real magickal work is done. That was a whole different conversation which I am not going into here.

Magic is sowing tiny seeds and giving them water, light and warmth and they grow into flowers or fruits and vegetables. These tiny seeds produce, in some cases massive plants. Trees and shrubs and in the vegetable garden pumpkins and marrows. Not to mention the wonderful magic of a new human life created from a seed that cannot even be seen with the naked eye.

I make wine. I have done for ever. It is fruit juice or vegetable juice with added sugar and yeast, the yeast reacts with the sugar and the wine ferments and hey presto about a year later you can drink it. If you do this in enough quantity some really weird magic will happen, you will fall down and the room will spin!

Magic is the baking of bread. Yet another yeast and sugar action. Baking cakes that rise from nothing. Have you ever watched a sponge cake mixture rise when cooked in a microwave? If not give it a try it sometime.

I make jams and chutneys to preserve foods, yet more magic.

Magic to me is the early morning sunrise. I love sunsets too but I must admit as I prefer the sunrise, sunsets, especially in the summer tend to be something I miss.

Magic is also the phases of the Moon and her effects upon our Planet, our tides and of course us. I like to plant my seeds to the phases of the moon too, this as I explained to Maisie is more everyday magic.

Magic is the turning of The Wheel of the ever changing ways of nature and the changing seasons. The colours of nature and the ever changing patterns of clouds in the sky. The anticipation of seeing the very first Snowdrop or Crocus to herald Spring after a long Winter. The magic of the first buds on the trees and then first leaves emerging. Then first flowers in the garden and on the beans and courgettes so that you know very soon you should be harvesting something good to eat. The magic of the leaves beginning to change colour in Autumn before they begin to fall. Of acorn and horse chestnut hunting, kicking the fallen leaves before we cycle down once again to the Winter.

Magic is spending time with family and good friends, especially those whose path is a similar one to ours. When we can spend time celebrating the turning of the Wheel and in better times sharing hugs and food and drink.

Magic to me is also the wonderful encounters we have had with wild creatures over the years on our walks, not always in the countryside but sometimes just on the edge of our seaside town.

One very magical wildlife encounter I experienced a few years ago was, I think so far at least, the most special.

It was early evening in mid December. I had finished work for the day and it was just about at twilight time. I got the dog from the office to take her for a short stroll before heading for home.

As ever I headed out for the canal towpath near to where I was working. As I reached the path another dog walker told me he had just seen two young Otters in the reeds. I quickly picked Flora up, as a terrier anything that moves is fair game to her. I waited patiently. I must explain that the canal has a bank, the towpath and then a run off ditch. I could see the grasses moving in the ditch then all seemed quiet. My sixth sense told me to look down and at my feet were the two young otters. They both looked up at the same time as I looked down. In perfect unison they backed up to where they had come from and then ran along the run off to the end and, much to the amazement of a guy walking towards me, ran across the towpath right in front of him and glided into the canal.

I have many times seen young otters and they always seem to move together, to surface from the water and to dive again it is as they use a form of telepathy to communicate.

Some of this I tried to explain to Maisie. I hope that she understood, or will begin to understand very soon, that magic is everywhere if you take the time to look for it and simple every day magic can be done by everyone.

So that to me is pure Magic!

A HALLOWEEN STORY

The waxing Hunter's Moon shone down fitfully between the drifting clouds. Lily sat in her room waiting for her parents to go to bed. She glanced at her watch. Ten thirty. It wouldn't be much longer. Lily was dreading the next few hours. She had joined in, very half heartedly, the Halloween party fun and had helped to give out sweets and other treats when the local children had come knocking on the door chanting, *"Trick or treat."*

As Lily waited to hear the sounds of her parents climbing the stairs and the usual bedtime bathroom routine she reflected upon how she had managed to get into this situation.

It had all begun in late August at Nat's eighteenth birthday come beginning university barbecue party. They had been chilling out in the garden enjoying a glass of wine after the usual barbecue fair of burnt sausages and underdone burgers. It was a hot afternoon, more like Midsummer than late August, when a wasp had landed on Lily's hand. Lily let out a terrified scream. "Wasp! Wasp!" "Just keep perfectly still it will fly away in a minute." "Stop stressing." "Oh for goodness sake what a ridiculous fuss over nothing." "It's only a wasp." Came the comments from her so called friends. Immediately Lily felt foolish. Yes it was a wasp but she was terrified of them or more accurately of getting stung.

"That's the trouble with you Lily you are afraid of everything." Said Nat. "No I'm not." Defended Lily. "It's just I don't like wasps at all." "Oh yes and mice, rats, bats and creepy crawlies in general." Retorted Nat.

This of course was true. Lily did have a fear of all the things Nat had listed. Lily had been told on several occasions she must be afraid of her own shadow. "Don't know why you are called Lily should have been Violet. Shrinking Violet." Was one of the more unkind things she had been taunted with in the past.

"I am not frightened of everything." Lily was trying not to show how upset she was but she could feel that tears were not far away. Lily's friend Becks could see how distressed she was becoming. "Come on who is for an ice cream. I hear the van in the next street this will be his next stop." Later after ice creams and another glass of wine Lily was feeling more relaxed. She was just beginning to enjoy the afternoon again when Nat began to taunt her once more.

"Had enough to eat and drink Scaredy Cat?" Lily felt the old fears begin again. "Yes. Thanks." Mumbled Lily. "Right Scaredy. Challenge time. Time to prove once and for all that you are not afraid of your own shadow. Time for you to face up to things." "Oh Nat don't be so cruel." Said Becks. "Lily can't help the way she is. Everyone has their fears. Things that they don't like. Even you I should imagine." "Huh. Me I'm afraid of nothing and no one. But old Scaredy. She is." "Please, please stop." Pleaded Lily. "That's right. I suppose you want to run for home now. Home to mummy and daddy." "Well it is beginning to get a bit late….." Began Lily. "Oh no, not until I set you a challenge." "Challenge. What challenge?" "Oh stop being so mean and cruel Nat." Becks interjected. "Can't even defend yourself now, got to get Becks to do it for you."

"Ok. I accept your challenge whatever it is." Agreed Lily miserably. She knew that if she didn't Nat's band of friends would never leave her alone. Becks looked at Nat and then at Lily. Becks knew how mean and cruel Nat could be having been a victim herself from time to time over the years.

"Right this is your challenge." Said Nat. "You spend the night alone in the Haunted House in the Haunted Wood at Halloween." Lily's heart skipped a beat. The haunted wood and the old house had a bad reputation. Lily hadn't been there since she was a child when she used to play there with Becks and Nat. She remembered they had been playing there one day and she had found a dead raven. Nat had said that if you found a dead raven you would die in the place where you had found the raven. Despite the heat of the afternoon Lily shivered at the memory. Nat saw Lily shiver. "See Scaredy won't do it. Too scared." "I am not at all scared, I can do it no problems." That was it. No going back. Challenge accepted.

Just then Lily heard her parent's bedroom door closing. She would just give them ten minutes to drift off to sleep and then it was time to leave.

Lily crept downstairs and collected her jacket and the small rucksack she had hidden earlier in the day. Lily thought she had better take some food and drink with her as the terror she had been feeling all day had manifested itself in the usual many trips to the bathroom. She was feeling dehydrated and empty already.

As Lily opened the back door the hinges gave their usual creak and groan. Very atmospheric, just what you need for Halloween she thought. The cloud cover had now lifted and the night was fairly light now. Light enough for Lily to see her way and not use the torch she had in her pocket. She would need that later in the wood as the tree cover was very dense and there would be little light.

Lily made her way to the boundary of the wood. She opened the gate and entered the wood. Lily felt as though she was being watched. The hairs at the nape of her neck stood on end and she shivered. "Come on girl. Get a grip. You have a long way and several hours to go yet."

As Lily entered the woods she was indeed being watched. Several pairs of eyes were on her. A vixen was hiding in a small copse and a family of badgers scurried into their sett to wait for the stranger to pass.

Lily took a deep breath. This was it. Challenge under way. The path was quite easy to begin with but after a very short time the path became overgrown with brambles and the tree roots protruded from the woodland floor, Lily had to be very careful not to trip and fall. The last thing she needed was a sprained ankle or worse.

Silently, behind Lily, the wolf crept from tree to tree. The moonlight glinting off its pale eyes. The wolf was watching Lily, watching her progress as she stumbled her way along the path to the middle of the wood towards the haunted house.

To call it a house was an overstatement. It was really a tumbled down cottage. At one time it had been the home of the woodsman and his family. But that was a long time ago when wealthy landowners had woodsmen come gamekeepers. Since the last gamekeeper and his family had left the place had fallen to rack and ruin. It had the reputation for being haunted because a body had been found hanging from one of the beams in the kitchen years ago. It was a local man who had murdered his wife and couldn't face the prospect of prison. Lily had heard the stories of how the man had been found, how his face was bloated and contorted and he was covered in maggots. Better not think about it thought Lily.

On and on she stumbled. Imagination running riot. An owl hooted and swooped down on silent wings. In the distance the vixen barked and screeched. Trees cast long black shadows and branches and tree roots caught at Lily's clothes and feet.

The wolf followed silently a few yards behind.

At last the cottage came into view. It was even more tumbled down than Lily remembered. Several slates were missing from the roof, windows were broken from being used as target practice by local vandals and the front door was almost hanging off it's hinges. As Lily approached all she could think about were rats, mice, bats and hanging corpses. Dare she go inside. Was it part of the challenge for her to actually go inside or could she stay outside for a few hours. Would anyone know? All of these questions were buzzing around in her brain when Lily was sure that she heard something or someone close by.

The wolf, as it had glided through the trees had dislodged a fallen branch and it had made a slight sound as it had fallen to the ground. That was the noise Lily had heard.

Lily looked behind her. She couldn't see anyone but perhaps it would be safer inside the cottage?

Slowly, reluctantly, Lily made her way to the dilapidated front door. Cautiously she pushed the door open. Lily switched on her torch and swept it around the hallway that lead to the kitchen. It seemed as though the place was empty. Just then the owl hooted again and glided silently into the cottage above Lily's head. Lily let out a scream and then realised that the owl was probably on it's way to it's roost as it must live in the old cottage. Lily crept into the cottage. There was a small sitting room to the right. Broken bits of old furniture littered the space. Suddenly Lily could here scampering footsteps and she just knew it had to be rats and mice. She could smell them too. Well who could fail to as they spent all day constantly peeing.

Lily made her way towards the kitchen at the back of the cottage.

The wolf had silently, slowly made its way to the front door of the cottage. It stood listening, head cocked to one side. Listening for Lily. An evil glint in it's eyes.

Lily carefully opened the kitchen door. A whoosh of air passed over her head. Lily ducked, her hands covering her head. It must be bats, loads of bats. As Lily rushed forward into the kitchen she saw something out of the corner of her eye. What…..was….that? By the light of her torch Lily saw a body suspended from a hook fixed to one of the beams on the ceiling. Lily screamed and screamed. As she turned to run out of the cottage ghostly groans and moans filled the air. As Lily ran cobwebs clawed at her face and covered her clothes. Lily ran and ran and didn't stop until she was some distance from the cottage. She could feel her heart pounding in her chest. Challenge or no challenge Lily was going to head for home. Tomorrow Lily was due to return to university. The only reason she was at home for the weekend was because her mother had got some theatre tickets ages ago for Lily's eighteenth.

Lily carefully made her way home along the twisting path taking care once again not to trip or hurt herself. She really didn't want to explain to her parents what she had been doing out in the woods alone in the dead of night.

When Lily reached home she let herself into the house as

quietly as possible. Drat that back door creaking again, she really should have oiled it. Stealthily she crept back upstairs to her room and exhausted climbed into bed. Her alarm was already set for six o'clock the following morning. If she was lucky she may get a few hours sleep.

At the cottage the wolf was howling with laughter. What a great gag. Nat would have so much to tell her mates over the next few days. The trip switch for the fan heater to come on and the ghostly groans and moans as Lily opened the kitchen door had worked a treat. As for the hanging dead body. What a laugh. Nat took down the fan heater and the "dead" body which was just a couple of stuffed pillow cases. She stashed them in one of the kitchen cupboards to be collected another time. Now time to head back to her room at university to load the phone video footage onto her laptop so that she could post to friends far and wide how she had fooled Scaredy Cat. How she had proved what a useless creature Lily was.

In her haste to get away Nat took a wrong path and didn't see the over growth of brambles and the dip in the ground. The next thing she knew she was in agony, both of her legs were broken. During the fall Nat's phone had flown from her hand and landed several yards away, then it slid along the ground before finally coming to rest inside a badger sett. Nat spent the rest of the night shouting for help but no one came due to the wood's bad reputation for being haunted. The locals kept well away at Halloween. Nat lay where she was all of the following day. Her parents were unconcerned because as far as they knew Nat was at a friends party at university. It was several days before anyone noticed that Nat was missing. There had been a very early bitterly cold spell followed by a heavy fall of snow.

The police set up an incident room at the university but after several weeks of fruitless enquiries the case was left open but unsolved.

Nat had changed into the wolf costume under the cover of darkness inside the wood before she lay in wait for Lily. She had stashed her bag with her clothes inside a hollowed out tree trunk. Unbeknown to Nat she was being watched by a guy with less than honest intentions who was in the area to try his luck at a little housebreaking. When Nat set off to follow Lily he retrieved the bag and pocketed her money. The designer jeans and tops he gave to his daughter who was thrilled to receive such a wonderful Christmas gift. The bag ended up in a local skip.

Ten years later.

The digger driver began to clear the massive area of brambles not far from the derelict cottage that someone had bought as their dream home. A doer upper as it is called. He was clearing the area to put in a septic tank. Suddenly he stopped. What was that? It looked like a tangle of old clothes or bits of fur. Perhaps it was an old fur coat that someone had buried years ago so as not to face the wrath of the anti fur folks. He climbed out of the digger cockpit and went to investigate.

"Police. How may we help you?"

Inspector Flynn arrived at the scene about an hour later. "Well what have we got here then?"

"A dead body Sir, its been here a good few years by the looks of it. We are waiting for the Pathologist to arrive. It's mostly just bones now after animals have been at it. There are some areas that may be identifiable, teeth possibly if we are lucky. The individual seems to have been wearing a wolf costume. Probably some kids at a fancy dress."

A Land Rover arrived. "Looks like the Pathologist now Sir." A woman got out of the vehicle and put on a protective suit and made her way to the scene.

"Good morning Inspector. I am the Pathologist. Lily Greaves. What do we have here then?"

Acknowledgements

Many thanks to Phil for all of your encouragement and the cups of camomile tea. It's not your fault that they were mostly cold when I remembered to drink them. Also thanks to Melanie and Tash at The Design Hive and to Alexa at Compass Publishing for the help and advice to a very novice writer. Thanks also to Eileen, Freda and Carole without their encouragement this project would never have gone ahead.

Printed in Great Britain
by Amazon